A NATURAL HISTORY OF IRELAND

A Natural History of Ireland

BY

CHRISTOPHER MORIARTY

THE MERCIER PRESS,

4 BRIDGE STREET, CORK

© Christopher Moriarty
SBN 85342 231 1

To

Patrick and Ruairi

CONTENTS

	Preface	7
1	Introduction	9
2	Cities, Towns and Suburbs	14
3	Rich Pasture	25
4	Poor Pasture	37
5	Forests	44
6	Wetlands and Bog	51
7	Inland Waters – Rivers	57
8	Inland Waters – Still Waters	65
9	Coast and Sea	74
10	The Coastal Counties	91
11	The Inland Counties	150
	Bibliography	174
	Index	176

PREFACE

There is so much information available about the plants and animals of Ireland that no person could hope to write a comprehensive account of them. Three people have made the attempt: Giraldus Cambrensis in 1188 produced his *Topography of Ireland*. William Thompson died in 1852 having completed three volumes on the subject and leaving notes which were published as a fourth. Robert Lloyd Praeger published a useful single volume work in 1950. Giraldus may be obtained in a delightful translation by John J. O'Meara; Thompson and Praeger are out of print. My book makes no claim to be as all-embracing as these three. It is a very brief outline of the subject and is written for the general rather than the specialist reader. For this reason English rather than scientific names have been used throughout and technical terms have been kept to the barest minimum.

The book is divided into two parts. The first half is a description of the country as a whole, arranged under headings of the main types of plant and animal habitats. The second part is a county by county guide, showing where the habitats described may be found. This is a highly personal account and tends to refer to the places which I consider to be the most interesting – other ecologists will no doubt be shocked by my selection. No maps are included in the book but all places named are given a National Grid reference and may be found on the Ordnance Survey ¼-inch sheets.

It is a pleasure to acknowledge the help which many of my friends have given. In particular I should mention Mr. Owen V. Mooney who advised on the forest sections, Professor J. N. R. Grainger who read parts of the manuscript, Mr. Fergus O'Gorman for a list of Seal haunts and Mr. Fergal Molloy for advice on Deer. Above all thanks go to my wife who not only endured the writing of the book but also read it in manuscript and made a great many invaluable criticisms.

1 INTRODUCTION

Ireland is an ancient country. Most of the land has stood above sea level since the Carboniferous era – before the Alps and Himalayas even existed. The only major exception to this is the north-east, in particular County Antrim, where the older rocks are covered by Tertiary lava flows. Land of such an age has had plenty of time to be worn down by the action of weather and this is why the mountains are relatively low and have gentle slopes as a rule. In spite of the great age of the solid rock, which lies beneath the soil everywhere and appears above its surface in many places, the most striking features of the land surface are of geologically recent arrival.

During the Great Ice Age, which began a million years ago and may still be with us, Ireland was for a time completely covered by glaciers. The slowly moving ice obliterated all forms of living things from the land and even filled the basin of the Irish Sea. It did much to carve out the mountains and valleys, giving most of them the form they have today. In enlarging and straightening the valleys the ice picked up and carried with it enormous quantities of stones and sand and left them scattered far and wide as it melted. This deposited material, called in general 'boulder clay' or 'glacial drift' now covers large areas of the country. In some places it forms ridges called 'eskers' and small hills averaging a third of a mile in length called 'drumlins'. In other parts it coats the older land surface. The drift material drains well. It seldom becomes waterlogged and forms the base of practically all the fertile land in the country.

The other great effect of the glaciation was to leave

Ireland connected to Britain and Britain to the Continent for some time. These connections persisted after the ice had begun to recede and plants and animals returned from the milder regions of the Continent. The level of the sea was rising slowly during this migration and eventually Ireland was cut off from Britain. This happened long before all of the species which might otherwise have lived here had arrived. So there are no snakes, no Wild Cat, and no Mole, to name a few. The lack of native freshwater fishes is even more striking. Pike, Rudd, Bream, Minnow and probably Perch have all been introduced by Man in the last thousand years and many of the most common species in Continental lakes and rivers are completely absent.

Five or six thousand years ago Man arrived in Ireland. The first inhabitants, the Mesolithic, were hunters and probably had relatively little influence on the flora and fauna. The next colonists, the Neolithic, on the other hand were farmers who brought their beasts, cattle, sheep, goats, pigs and dogs and their crops, wheat and barley. They required land for crops and for their grazing animals so they set to work to clear the forests which covered much of the land when they arrived. From that time, four or five thousand years ago, the native plants and animals of Ireland were gradually reduced and replaced by those brought in by the settlers. One more great natural event took place. This was a change to a wetter climate about 500 B.C. The new climate permitted the development of peat over a wide area, especially on the Atlantic coast and in the badly drained centre of the country. In many places the peat grew amongst the trees in the ancient forests and their stumps may be seen to this day in the cut-away bog. Whether this change in climate was entirely natural or whether it was caused to

Ancient Forest. The stumps of trees which were killed thousands of years ago by the invading peat are revealed in modern times when the peat is cut away for fuel.

some extent by the felling and burning of the forests by primitive Man is not known. Since then the climate has become drier and very little new peat is now being formed.

Until very recent times Man has been engaged in fighting with nature. Animals other than the domestic ones were competitors and had to be destroyed. Water prevented the use of land so drains were built to carry it away as quickly as possible. There were so many wars and changes of land ownership that timber was a risky investment so trees were cut down and the forest lands were turned over to grazing for quicker returns. The results of the effects of geology, climate and human development leave our land as it is now, in 1970. Much good has been done. If the country were still in its state of primeval forest on the dry land with peat bog on the wet it would not be able to keep a population of over four million people well fed and housed.

However, humanity has now reached a stage of development when our powers of destroying our natural resources are enormously greater than they were as little as fifty years ago. Chain saws and crawler tractors can remove forest and drain land. Poisons can control insects. Firearms and fast transport can decimate almost any of our species of wild animals. Nature no longer stands as a menace in Ireland but we are quite capable of destroying much that we love. The destruction will not be brought about deliberately, it can take us by surprise. Nobody wanted to poison hundreds of Salmon on the River Blackwater in October 1969. By taking steps now we can keep our beautiful land and waters in their present state and even improve them in places. We cannot achieve this by acting blindly, nor by leaving the matter entirely in the hands of the small but dedicated band of conservationists who are already fully conscious of what must be done. They need the willing support of the public who must first be told about what we have to preserve. The pages that follow give a bare outline of the plants and animals of Ireland as they are today. The first half of the book deals with the basic principles as they apply to the country as a whole. The second half is a county by county guide to what I consider the most interesting regions. This part is necessarily a highly personal choice. Not one single square yard of Ireland is without interest and the task of describing the whole country in a short book is one of brutal rejection of many exciting places.

This book deals mainly with the 'higher' plants and animals. Most of the species of plants in this category are the 'flowering plants' – a term which includes many with inconspicuous flowers such as grasses, rushes, and many water weeds. The others are the coniferous trees and the ferns. These plants cover practically all of the land surface and also dominate the rivers and the shallower parts of lakes. They are virtually unable to survive in the sea where lower plants, the algae, dominate.

The higher animals are the 'vertebrates' – animals with backbones which include mammals, birds, reptiles, amphibians and fishes. The other animals, infinitely more numerous but probably less in bulk on the surface of the earth, are the 'invertebrates' – shellfish, insects, worms, to name but a few of the best known, together with a host of creatures invisible to the naked eye.

In Ireland there are rather few mammals, the only large native land species surviving is the Red Deer. Bear, Wolf and Wild Pig among others were once plentiful. Birds are the most noticeable wild creatures and more then 350 species have been recorded though not many more than one hundred of these are common. There is one resident reptile, the Common Lizard and a few visitors – turtles from the Americas which get stranded from time to time. The amphibians number three: the Frog, the Natterjack Toad and the Newt. There are seventeen freshwater fishes of which not more than three are undoubted natives. About 200 species of sea fishes are known to visit our shores.

Plants and animals live in 'communities' – a particular kind of soil in a particular climate will support plants of certain types which in turn attract a particular group of animals. There are many such communities in Ireland and the next few chapters describe the main ones. The pattern in each is to begin with the most barren kind of region in the community and work towards the most productive.

2 CITIES, TOWNS AND SUBURBS

There is a tendency for people who live or study in towns to try to escape from them to study wild life. This is understandable – the obvious places to look for wild things are those where Man has the least influence. However it is very interesting to see how a variety of plants and animals have adapted themselves to more or less artificial surroundings.

The most extreme cases of artificial environments are the insides of clean, new buildings. Several species of flies and other insects enter in search of food or dazzled by lights at night. Some beetles will also survive and may breed; their abundance depends to a great extent on whether there is a kitchen or canteen in the building. A small office block in which nobody eats sandwiches makes about the poorest possible habitat.

From this there is a gradual progression through older and dirtier buildings. Wherever food is kept and tends to be left in the open more creatures make their appearance. If there are plenty of flies spiders will establish themselves and thrive. Then, where the food storage is on a relatively large scale rats and mice appear. There is only one native Irish species, the Wood Mouse or Long-tailed Field Mouse. The House Mouse was introduced by Man in the distant past and the Brown Rat appeared in the eighteenth century. House Mouse and Brown Rat depend in Ireland on the presence of humans and are very scarce or unknown far from houses or places like the seashore, where there is plenty of human waste.

Outside the buildings the environment changes. Rooftops and areas such as docklands and railway stations are the most barren but even they offer very much more than the interiors. Soil develops in many different places. On rooftops over the years dust piles up in corners and sooner or later seeds of some plants arrive there. The plants are normally species with wind-borne seeds and include a number of grasses and Groundsel. Similar plants establish themselves on the ground in places where dirt accumulates. On old walls where the plaster or pointing is crumbling several species of fern grow. Wall Rue, Rusty-back and Spleenwort actually thrive on walls, others, like Bracken and Hart's-tongue, survive but usually in a rather stunted form.

Sparrow, Pigeon, Starling and small numbers of Pied Wagtail are the birds of these regions. Sparrow and Pigeon owe their success to being prepared to come very close to humans. They are therefore able to be the first animals to secure such waste food as supernumerary sandwiches. They also get supplies of undigested grain from horse droppings. Starling thrive because they can eat almost any kind of food, animal or vegetable. Pied Wagtail feed on small insects which are plentiful wherever there is any refuse. In summer the Swift is a common species. It nests in holes in buildings and feeds entirely on insects caught on the wing. The Swift even collects its nesting material, in the form of feathers and dried grasses, in the air and very rarely settles on the ground.

Wherever there is open soil, rather than concrete and slates, plants grow in profusion and they support a much larger and more varied fauna. Even in the centres of cities there are roadside trees, gardens, parks, cemetries, river or canal banks and waste land. Going out from the city centre the size of the gardens increases until finally the open country appears. We are fortunate in Ireland in the small size of our cities. Not one of them is so large

that it takes more than half an hour's bus ride to reach the open spaces.

In the parks and gardens the environment is largely artificial. Lawns contain many species of native grasses and flowers but their character would change completely in less than a year if they were not cut regularly. Flower beds are filled for the most part with plants which would not thrive under natural conditions in our climate. Some native trees and shrubs, such as Holly and Hawthorn, are popular in shrubberies but introduced plants are favoured. The open soil between plants in beds is completely unnatural – such soil becomes colonized in a matter of weeks in summer with a rich variety of weeds which must be removed all too regularly to preserve the planted flowers. Cemetries are tended like parks but have an added advantage in their solitude. It is possible to spend long periods in them with very little in the way of living human beings for company. This advantage is slightly reduced by the fact that birds are much more tame and easy to approach in crowded parks than in places where they are less accustomed to intruders. River and canal banks often provide good areas where natural vegetation grows undisturbed or with nothing more than periodical cutting of the grass. Land laid waste for a year or two by demolition of a building or by the abandoning of a garden makes an exceptionally interesting habitat where the gradual invasion of weeds can be studied. Two kinds of plant make up the majority of weeds. The members of one type have a flattened growth and therefore thrive in places where they may be walked on – as their leaves

Seed Dispersal. The seeds of plants like the Dandelion are carried considerable distances by the wind and the plants establish themselves quickly on waste land.

grow down on the ground they are not liable to be knocked over. Examples are the Daisy, Dandelion and Germander Speedwell. They are also so low that they are passed over by lawn mowers. The others are 'annual' plants which grow up from seed and come to flower inside a year. They are the weeds which invade open ground, especially the soil in well-tended flower beds. Shepherd's Purse, Groundsel and Nettle are a few. In the waste land larger species thrive: Willow Herb, Sow Thistle, Hawkweed and docks are common and others, such as thistles of various kinds appear from time to time.

Mammals, apart from the Brown Rat and the two species of Mouse, are few in city areas. Fallow Deer may be seen in the largest parks. Rabbit and Hare are sometimes common. Bats may be plentiful. The Fox is one of the most interesting and appears to be on the increase. It is a scavenger and also eats many small mammals including Rat and Mouse. Dustbins and rubbish heaps provide it with both scraps and small mammals. The Fox is not yet known to breed in built-up areas in Ireland but it is common on the outskirts of cities and regularly makes foraging expeditions inside.

The most plentiful kinds of garden birds are those which feed on the ground and rest or shelter in trees or bushes. Robin, Blackbird, Song Thrush and Chaffinch are found in nearly all parts. Greenfinch and Bullfinch are more restricted in distribution. The Robin nests in holes, the others build open nests in bushes and all are able to find plenty of suitable sites, even in small walled gardens. Where there is more open ground and tall trees Rook, Jackdaw, Magpie, Mistle Thrush, Hedge Sparrow and Wood Pigeon are added to the list. In the breeding season these birds feed on insects, worms and other invertebrates but from autumn to spring their diet includes plant material such as fruit and seeds and bread. Most of them will come to feed at bird tables. Rook, Magpie, Mistle Thrush and Pigeon build open nests in trees. The Jackdaw uses a hole in a wall or in a tree and the Hedge Sparrow builds an open nest in a shrub or sometimes on top of a wall.

Great Tit, Blue Tit and Wren find most of their food above the ground. They are primarily insect eaters and hunt for insects and spiders amongst the branches of trees. As most of the insects live on the lower sides of the branches the tits have developed great skill in hanging upside-down. Tits also like fats and have discovered how to peck through the covers of milk bottles to reach the cream. Tits and Wren nest in holes in trees or walls and occasionally in unlikely places such as letter boxes. A number of insect-eating birds come for the summer only. The commonest garden species are Chiffchaff and Willow Warbler which hunt for small insects in bushes and trees.

Various seagulls are important as scavengers in cities. They never take up permanent residence but fly in to look for scraps. They are found in their greatest concentrations on rubbish heaps. Herring Gull is the commonest. In the more open spaces, such as playing fields, Black-headed Gull and Common Gull are also found. They and occasional wading birds such as Oyster-catcher and Lapwing feed on worms and grubs which they find in soft soil.

Water adds a further dimension to city wildlife. There are rivers, canals and ponds, estuaries and seaside, clean water and dirty. Even rainwater tanks have their own particular inhabitants. The water in and around towns and cities is polluted to some degree. Pollution results in some cases from the presence in the water of actively toxic chemicals. Cyanide, from electro-plating works, is an example. The more common cause – and one which is much harder to combat – is the build-up of organic wastes which use up oxygen as they are broken down by bacteria.

In large population centres domestic sewage is the main offender. Sewage systems in many parts of the country are hopelessly antiquated and, in any case, fail to collect all of the sewage. In many towns the houses and even hotels which back on to the local river discharge all their waste directly into it. In others the sewage is treated before it reaches the rivers but the treatment plant is not always big enough to deal with everything that comes. In addition, there are many categories of factories which discharge large quantities of organic material. Creameries and slaughterhouses are amongst the worst.

Rivers which flow downstream of industrial complexes give the most extreme cases of pollution. The water is usually cloudy and often stinking. Very few animals are able to live in it. The dominant ones are the larvae of certain species of Chironomid midges. They are bright red, worm-like grubs which dwell in the mud. Certain small annelid worms are also able to survive. Rats are usually plentiful. Mammals, which get their oxygen supply from the air rather than from the water are well able to swim in even the most heavily polluted conditions.

Moving upstream from the barren areas the river waters become clearer and water plants are able to grow. The types of plant depend on the speed of flow and on the depth of the water. In rapid stretches the plant life is mostly composed of moss-like species which make use of stones and other irregularities to give them some shelter from the current. There are also several kinds of Water Buttercup with tassels of hair-like leaves which offer very little resistance to the flow. These have white flowers with yellow centres and make a fine show in summer. In slower waters mud settles on the river bed and many species of plants can root and grow. These have upright stems and relatively large leaves. Brooklime, Water Dropwort, Water Cress and Mare's Tail are a few of the common ones. Where the water is slow and deep, especially in the canals, the Yellow Water Lily is a dominant plant.

These weeds give support to a marvellous variety of animal life. The emphasis is on the word 'support'. Unlike the higher plants on land those in the water are not grazed to any marked extent except by a few birds such as Coot, Moorhen and Swan. The larger water plants

Mallard. The commonest breeding species of duck in Ireland. The brightly coloured drake in the foreground takes no part in sitting on the eggs, this is left to the duck with her subdued brown colouring.

provide an attachment for a variety of small types, mainly green algae. These are food for many kinds of invertebrates, especially the water snails and a host of microscopic animals. The members of the microfauna are in turn eaten by insects and other comparatively large creatures – in general known as the 'macro-fauna'. There are many groups of which the mayflies, chironomids, freshwater shrimps and water lice are amongst the more important. These animals either shelter in the mud or creep or swim amongst the plants. Finally at the top of the food chain within the water are the fishes.

Minnow, which were introduced to Ireland within the last thousand years or so, and Stickleback which are native, are the most easily seen. Minnow generally live in shoals, Stickleback are solitary and have extremely interesting nestbuilding habits. The male builds a barrel-shaped nest and guards the eggs and young. Larger species are Perch and Gudgeon. The Perch is widely distributed in Ireland, the Gudgeon is rather local. Pike may sometimes be seen lurking amongst reeds, waiting to pounce on passing fish. Trout are most often seen when they rise for insects on the surface. The Eel is very common but usually hunts at night. Salmon and Sea Trout pass through the rivers in many towns, especially near the sea. Their young feed in the rivers but the adults come in from the sea mainly to spawn in upstream gravel.

Ponds and reservoirs in towns, being artificial, usually have less to offer than the rivers and canals. In particular there tend to be fewer species of fishes. The insect variety is as good as in the open waters because practically all of the species are able to fly as adults and can move from water to water. The freshwater environment is one of the most rewarding to study because it offers,

Heron. A fish-eating bird and our largest land bird. As one of the finest birds in the country it deserves protection. The damage it does to stocks of wild fish is probably grossly exaggerated.

within a confined space, a wide range of plant and animal life, every organism depending to a great extent on the others. The same is true of other environments but they tend to be larger and much more difficult to understand.

The Moorhen is the commonest resident water bird in city ponds and canals. It feeds on water weed and seeds and nests by the water's edge, usually amongst reeds or flags. The closely related Coot prefers larger areas of water and is less common in urban areas. The Mallard has adapted itself very well to city life and may nest high up on buildings besides the more usual sites on the ground and close to the water. Mute Swan, which were originally introduced to Ireland as domestic fowl, nest on the banks of canals and broad rivers. Gulls use the open water both to hunt for refuse and to rest on and preen their feathers. Herring Gull and Black-headed Gull are common. The Great Black-back is widespread but never in numbers and the Lesser Black-back is a local summer visitor. The Kingfisher is scarcer than it used to be, probably because the building of retaining walls and the developing of the river banks is reducing the extent of steep, sandy or muddy banks which it needs for nesting. The Grey Wagtail, which feeds on insects caught near the water, and the Dipper which hunts beneath the surface, are common in some places. Heron and Cormorant search for fish. The Cormorant swims in the larger rivers. The Heron stands and waits by the shore. It nests in tall trees in the Dublin suburbs.

In spite of pollution the tidal parts of city rivers are often rich in fish life. Flounder are common in the mud in many rivers and Grey Mullet may be seen swimming near the surface. Shore Crabs and many species of worms also inhabit the mud and Mussels grow attached to harbour walls. Apart from the absence of certain species due to pollution the seashore close to cities is similar to the shore elsewhere and will be described in a later chapter.

3 RICH PASTURE

This chapter describes the rich country. Most of it is used as pasture, for grazing cattle and sheep. A secondary use of the rich land is the production of crops other than grass. Most of our crops are grown in a cycle of a year or less. The cereals and many of the roots are planted as seed. Others, like potatoes, are sown as tubers. The ground is prepared for planting crops by ploughing which turns the pre-existing grass sward over, killing the grass and most of the weeds and leaving the soil ready for the crop to grow without undue competition. As a rule all of the land used in tillage is turned back to grass land as part of the normal rotation programme. The rich land is nearly all low-lying and confined to regions where the rock had a thick covering of glacial drift material.

The only barren areas in the rich lowlands are the surfaces of roads. Busy roads support even less living material than do walls and rooftops. The mosses and lichens which gain a foothold on concrete and roof tiles are completely unable to survive the wear and tear from the wheels of cars. Very soon after a road gets abandoned plants succeed in growing and even a good metalled surface gets obliterated after some years. This action can be seen where corners are bypassed in road improvement schemes. No animals can live permanently on the metalled surfaces but several species of birds do find a certain amount of food there. The Pied Wagtail is the most successful. It catches insects on the road and beside it and manages to move quickly enough to avoid being struck by fast cars. Rook, Starling and Sparrow come to the roads to feed on spilled grain and material from horse and cattle dung. In contrast to the roads, the verges are rich in interest.

When extensive road widening operations are in progress large areas of ground are stripped bare. Under natural conditions such bare earth is uncommon – landslides and the uprooting of trees are the usual causes. Earth never remains bare for long; it is rapidly colonized by plants which grow from seeds either carried on the wind or dropped by birds. Dandelion, Hawkweeds, Sow Thistle and various true Thistles together with a variety of grasses are amongst the first arrivals. The first few are all members of the same Family, the Compositae, and their seeds are attached to umbrella-like structures which allow them to be carried long distances by the wind. The grass seeds may not travel so far but spread from the roadside pastures. A regular, often abundant, plant on the bare earth is the Poppy, and many small annuals like Shepherd's Purse also arrive. The annuals can live in regions like these only for a year or two before being overwhelmed by the permanent cover of perennial plants. These include Vetches, Dog Daisy and Buttercups amongst many others. The particular interest of the roadside plants is that they are not subject to grazing or disturbance to the same extent as the wild plants of the neighbouring fields. It is therefore possible to get an idea of how the vegetation of the open spaces would develop in the absence of Man and his animals.

Except in the places where the roadsides have been disfigured by concrete or chain-link fences hedges dominate the rich pasture land. With the advent of mechanical hedge cutters they have become a little more orderly in appearance than in the past but they still have a pleasantly unkempt air. The hedges represent a reduction of the scrub vegetation that might otherwise cover the well-drained glacial gravels. Hawthorn is a dominant species but Bramble, Wild Rose and Blackthorn are common. Trees, especially Ash and Sycamore develop naturally in the hedges. Other roadside trees are usually planted artificially.

Cultivation creates entirely artificial conditions. Broadleaved crops such as Sugar Beet and Potato create a great deal of shade and prevent the development of wild plants. Cereal crops usually have a fair proportion of weeds amongst them. The Poppy is especially noticeable but Thistles and various grasses appear as well. Whatever the crop, worms and insects thrive in the soil. Some, like the Earthworm, live on dead organic material and are beneficial in accelerating the breakdown of the dead leaves and roots which releases nitrogen and other elements necessary to the growth of the crops. Others, like the Leather-jackets (larva of Craneflies), feed on living roots and do a considerable amount of damage. When the land is being ploughed or harrowed many of these invertebrates are brought to the surface and attract a host of birds. Rook, Jackdaw, Starling, Herring Gull and Blackheaded Gull come in large numbers. Small species like Pied Wagtail and Meadow Pipit and most of the hedgerow birds also follow the plough.

The pastures themselves are dominated by grasses. There are many species: Cocksfoot, Perennial Rye Grass, Yorkshire Fog, Crested Dogstail, Catstail, Wild Barley, Quaking Grass are a few of the commonest and most easily recognized. Clovers are highly desirable grazing plants, providing both good food for the stock and increasing the available nitrogen in the soil by the action of bacteria in their root nodules. Thistles, Ragwort and Buttercups are undesirable weeds but thrive because the grazing stock will not eat them unless on the

Grazing. Trees in parkland are shaped by cattle and deer which eat the leaves. The lower branches on the left hand side of this Chestnut curve downwards to follow a dip in the ground; all leaves within reach of the cattle are eaten.

verge of starvation. The Buttercups are perennial plants, growing up year after year from buried roots. Thistles and Ragwort are biennials, growing from seed. In their first year of life they form a rosette of leaves on the ground which persists through the winter. The following year they send up flowering stems. Thistles are generally confined to rich land and are considered to be an indication of fertility. Ragwort is more tolerant of poor conditions and is a highly dangerous weed to livestock. It contains a number of poisonous alkaloids which cause a fatal liver disease. It is illegal to permit it to grow but the law seldom appears to be enforced.

Properly controlled grazing of land, with regular cutting of the weeds maintains a good pasture. The Curragh of Kildare is a beautiful example. Overgrazing leads to the reduction of the grass and a build-up of weeds. Undergrazing can be quite as damaging to a pasture. It allows shrubs like Gorse and Hawthorn to gain a foothold and, once they have begun to grow, they are difficult to check. Where the grazing is just at the right intensity the seedling bushes never get a chance to develop. Grazing also prevents the development of trees from seed.

Trees in the rich pasture regions are usually confined to places where the grazing animals have been kept out. They survive in hedgerows because the thorns of the neighbouring bushes protect them in their early years. Otherwise most trees are found close to houses, in places fenced off from the stock. The magnificent Chestnut, Beech, Oak and Sycamore trees which stand in the best parkland have all been carefully preserved in their first years. The seedlings are enclosed by railings until they have grown so high that the animals cannot reach all of the leaves. As the branches spread out the cattle reach up as high as they can to eat the shoots and this is why such trees have no branches below about six feet. Old cemetries often have many fine Yew trees growing. There are two theories as to why this should be so. One is that these trees with their poisonous leaves were planted so that farmers would make sure that their beasts would not stray amongst the graves. According to the other, the wood of the yew was needed for archers' bows and the cemetries were the only places where the trees could be planted without danger to the cattle.

Animal life is comparatively sparse in the very open lands. The Meadow Pipit is one of the few birds that can nest safely in comparatively short grass. In winter wading birds such as Lapwing and Curlew come to hunt for invertebrates when the weather is wet and the ground soft but they move to rough or damp land for breeding.

Rook, Jackdaw, Starling, various gulls and thrushes also feed there. However, such wide open spaces are rare in Ireland and usually there are plenty of hedges and ditches, rough land with scrub or wet land with rushes, houses, walls, trees and other forms of cover. The character of such areas with small fields is quite different from the large grasslands. The cover and high perches that hedges and trees provide enable many more kinds of animals to live in the fields amongst them. This kind of cover is essential to the smaller birds and mammals which will not readily feed on the ground at any great distance from it.

The land mammals of Ireland are furtive creatures. For long generations Man or his Dog or both have tried to kill them for food or because they were regarded as intolerable competitors. The Wolf was actually hunted to extinction in the eighteenth century and the surviving mammals owe their existence to their small size and their ability to keep well hidden in the daytime. The only large mammal is the Red Deer and it lives as a native only in Killarney where it has been protected for a long period.

Four classes of mammals are represented. The bats are the least well known but have the largest number of species, seven in all. At least three, the Long-eared, the Pipistrelle and Leisler's are common but since it is virtually impossible to identify bats on the wing the status and distribution of the various species is not well known. All of the Irish species are insect-eaters and are active from dusk to dawn in the warmer months of the year. In the daytime they sleep hanging upside-down in old buildings. Most of our species mate at the end of the summer but do not give birth to their young before the following spring.

There are two species of insectivores, the Pygmy Shrew and the Hedgehog. The Shrew is the smallest mammal in the country. It is probably very common in rich land but it keeps very well concealed and is rarely seen except when cats bring it in. The Hedgehog is also nocturnal but is sometimes active in the daytime. It is a rather slow-moving beast, relying on its coat of prickles for protection. Unfortunately it cannot move quickly enough to avoid cars and very large numbers are killed on country roads every year. In spite of this it is a common enough species. Shrew and Hedgehog hibernate during the winter months when food is scarce, as do the bats. Hibernation is not like normal sleep but entails a lowering of the body temperature and a general slowing down of all of the life activities such as breathing. Disturbing a hibernating animal usually kills it because it is not able to adjust itself to waking life without going through a period of preparation. Animals like Hedgehog which may be found when hibernating in places such as garden rubbish heaps should be left to sleep in peace if possible.

The native rodents found in rich open land are the Wood Mouse and the Mountain Hare. Two species have been introduced, the Brown Hare and the Rabbit. Until the introduction of myxomatosis in 1953 the Rabbit was by a long way the most familiar wild mammal. The numbers have recovered in places but it is still uncommon in many regions where is was well known before. Some of the coastal islands have Rabbit populations which were never infected. The Rabbit rests and breeds in burrows and has many litters in the course of a year. Hares live permanently in the open and breed less often. Their resting places are known as 'forms'. The young hares are left in these and rely on their cryptic colouration and habit of keeping perfectly still for safety from predators.

The three carnivores of the rich pasture are the Fox, the Badger and the Stoat (known everywhere as the 'Weasel', though the true Weasel is not found in Ireland). All three have bad and largely unmerited reputations as 'vermin'. They are known to eat the eggs and young of game birds on occasion but it is unlikely that their predation in this respect does any material damage to the stocks – human poachers and domestic cats probably do far greater damage. Detailed studies of Fox have shown that it rarely kills healthy lambs. The Badger's most important food item is the Earthworm but it eats a great variety of other things including rats and mice, beetles and fallen fruits. Stoat live mainly on rats, mice and young rabbits. All three hunt in open ground but prefer to rest in woods or other places where there is good cover. The Fox's hole is called the 'earth', the male Fox is a 'dog' and the female a 'vixen', the young are 'cubs'. The Badger's burrow which may be quite a labyrinth of tunnels, is called a 'set', the male is a 'boar', the female a 'sow' and the young are 'cubs'.

The mammals described in this chapter are by no means confined to the lowland pasture regions but are found there in their greatest numbers. The pasture is in all respects the most productive part of the land and can therefore support the greatest quantities of wild plants and the largest numbers of the animals that depend on them. The standing crop of plants in bog and mountain regions is so much lighter and slower growing that they cannot support the same numbers of dependent creatures.

The great majority of the birds of the lowland pastures are species which feed on the ground and rest

Ragworth tastes unpleasant and is not normally eaten by grazing animals. It therefore stands up amongst the edible grasses in pastureland.

above it. The hedges and trees provide both resting places and nesting sites for them and the numbers both of species and individual birds bear a very close relationship of the number of hedges. The garden birds (p. 18) are all found here and a number of species besides. The Yellow Hammer is a conspicuous bird on roadside hedges which it leaves to search for insects and fallen seeds on the ground. The Goldfinch, one of the most beautiful of small birds, feeds to a large extent on the seeds of plants like thistles. It is light and agile enough to perch on the flower heads and pick the seeds before the fall. The Linnet is another hedgerow bird, frequently feeding on the ground or on seed heads. In some winters substantial mixed flocks of finches roam the country, going from field to field and feeding on weed seeds. Chaffinch, Greenfinch, Yellow Hammer, Linnet and Redpoll may all be seen together.

Wood Pigeon, Rook, Magpie and Hooded Crow nest in tall trees, the Rooks in closely-knit colonies, usually close to farms. Their preference for farms depends more on the fact that suitable trees are most frequent close to dwellings rather than on any close connection between Rook and Man. In regions where trees are scarce the rookeries tend to be very large and the birds have a wider feeding range. Wood Pigeon are solitary breeders but form large flocks outside the breeding season – these flocks are increased by winter visitors from Britain and the Continent. Magpie and Hooded Crow are normally solitary birds all their lives, the pair rather than the flock being the unit of population.

Jackdaw and Starling are gregarious birds but the individual pairs nest at some distance from each other. This is because they both require holes to hide their nests in and holes, such as chimneys, hollow trees and gaps in walls or roofs seldom occur close together.

The Thrushes, a group which includes Robin and Blackbird as well as Song Thrush and Mistle Thrush have strong territorial instincts and as a rule chase other individuals of their own species away. This habit breaks down after the breeding season amongst Mistle Thrushes which regularly go about in flocks in the autumn. In winter two northern species of thrush, Fieldfare and Redwing come from Iceland and Scandinavia and normally wander about in flocks. Early in the winter they feed on berries such as Hawthorn but later on hunt in the fields for soil invertebrates.

Other birds keep to the hedges and trees, seldom or never going to the ground in search of food. These are the Great, Blue and Coal Tits, the Tree Creeper and the Goldcrest which stay throughout the year and the Willow Warbler, Chiffchaff and Whitethroat which come for the summer. The basic food of all these birds is insects and spiders, caught by hunting amongst the leaves or in crevices in the bark of trees. With the exception of the Tree Creeper they can also feed on soft fruits and the Tits are almost omnivorous. Two popular game birds, Pheasant and Partridge keep to the ground but require the cover of hedges or copses for breeding and shelter.

The strictly insectivorous birds can survive here only in the summer. Swallow and House Martin are the best known. They feed entirely on the wing but rest on perches such as overhead wires and collect mud and dead grasses for nesting material from the ground. Swallows usually nest indoors in barns or stables, House Martins build in the open beneath the eaves of houses and sometimes under bridges or on overhanging cliffs. Swifts live almost entirely in the air, seldom coming to land except to visit their nests. The Spotted Flycatcher also hunts for insects in the air but operates by waiting on a perch and flying out when it sees one passing.

Finally there are the predatory birds, those that feed on other birds or on mammals. They belong to two groups, the Hawks and the Owls. The Kestrel is the commonest hawk and is a member of the Falcon tribe. Falcons search for their prey from a height and usually capture it by flying downwards. The Kestrel is unusual in doing without a perch but keeping to a fixed position above the ground by hovering. The hovering consists of flying into the wind but at exactly the same speed as it so that the bird does not move in relation to the ground. The Kestrel feeds more on beetles and other large insects than on vertebrates but takes mice and small birds as well. The Merlin, another Falcon, is not so common and feeds mainly on birds, again captured from above. The Sparrow Hawk is fairly common but less so than the Kestrel. It perches in hedges and flies out suddenly at passing birds, chasing them from behind rather than from above.

Most Owls hunt by dusk or after dark and can find their prey by highly accurate sound location as well as by sight. Two species are fairly common, the Barn Owl and the Long-eared Owl. They feed mainly on small mammals such as rats and mice. The Barn Owl lives in sheds and lofts and is usually found close to farmyards where its prey is plentiful. It is one of the few birds in Ireland that has no fixed nesting season and breeds whenever food is abundant. The Long-eared Owl is more a bird of the open, roosting in trees. Owls are much less common in Ireland than in other European countries, probably bacause there are so very few species of small mammals available.

4 POOR PASTURE

Most of the fertile land of Ireland is found at low levels where the glacial deposits of easily-drained gravelly material are thick. Wherever the gravels lie on the slopes of mountains it is easy to see the line of their highest extent. On the gravel the grass is green at all times of the year, the fields are usually rather small and divided by hedges and many of them are under cultivation. On the higher land Bracken or Heather dominate the drier parts while sedges and coarse moorland grasses grow in damper places. In winter most of these plants die down and the hills take on shades of brown and purple. Peat bog is present on many of these slopes and bare rock often shows. The large boulders which are found on mountain sides have usually been deposited by glaciers but have seldom been carried over great distances. In the west where the rainfall is higher and the drift material scarcer these conditions are found down to sea level as well as on the hills.

The soil is poor, deficient in lime, nitrogen and other important elements. These extreme conditions limit both the variety of plants which can grow there and the quantity of vegetation produced. Very few of the 'rich pasture' plants are found in any abundance. The plants which do thrive owe much of their success to being tough or otherwise unpalatable to grazing animals. The traditional small farms on this land cannot provide their owners with a reasonable income for modern living. It does, however, lend itself to large scale sheep-ranching, to intensive farming and to forestry. It also has virtually untapped possibilities for recreation.

The great attraction of this type of ground lies in the

Violet. One of several purple species which grow in spring in woodland and hedges, taking advantage of the time before the larger plants come into leaf.

limited variety of plants and animals that can be found In the rich lowlands there is such a profusion of living things that it is comparatively difficult to study the effects that the various species have on each other. In the poor lands there are so few species to consider that it is a much simpler matter to decide why a particular one thrives in one place and not in the next. The uplands also have the advantage that on account of their poverty the human population is low and the degree of interference with the natural flora and fauna is limited.

On the poor land trees are scarce as natural vegetation. The Mountain Ash is one of the most widely spread. In valleys where there is a little shelter Holly, Willow and Alder may be found. Otherwise the plants are mostly low and small. Heather is a common dominant plant. There are several small orchids with white or mauve flowers, Tormentil and Lousewort also grow amongst the heather. On damp open patches cotton grass blooms and one of the finest plants is the bright yellow Bog Asphodel. In the west the Royal Fern is common. The most remarkable plant species are the Sundews and Butterworts which capture and digest insects on their leaves. There are three species of each. The Common Butterwort and Roundleaved Sundew are found in damp places in most parts of the country. The Great Butterwort, also called Bog Violet, is abundant in the south-west. The butterworts have rosettes of greenish-yellow leaves which are sticky and supplied with glands which secrete digestive juices. The leaves of the sundews are more elaborate, being reddish and covered with tentacles which are sticky at the tips. As soon as an insect catches on one or two of the tentacles the leaf curls up so that others are brought into play. These insect-eating plants use photo-synthesis to make their food as do other green plants. The insects are used as a source of nitrogen and other elements which are scarce in the bog.

Ground mammals are as varied as in the richer regions but far less plentiful. Fox, Badger, Stoat, Hares, Rabbit, Hedgehog and Pygmy Shrew are all to be found. Rats and mice occur where there are human dwellings but as these are few and far between the dependent animals are also scarce. Bats are rather uncommon on account of the lack of suitable roosting places. The Red Deer, the only surviving native species, is reasonably common in the Killarney region. Red Deer, introduced from Scotland are found in other regions. Fallow Deer and Japanese Sika Deer, both imported species, are quite widely distributed.

These regions are often rather silent and depressing in winter. Apart from sheep there is very little sign of life. Birds are very scarce, the smaller species having moved to lower ground. On the heathery slopes Grouse is a permanent resident. It was formerly a common species but on account of uncontrolled burning of the heather and too much shooting it has become relatively scarce. Heather shoots and other moorland plants form the greater part of its diet. In the damper parts Snipe and sometimes Woodcock may be found. They have long bills and hunt for worms and other soil invertebrates by probing in the mud. Both of them feed mainly at night and keep hidden by day so that they are seldom seen until their resting places, amongst tussocks of grass or rushes, are disturbed. Raven and Hooded Crow fly overhead occasionally, on the lookout for dead animals. The only mammals likely to be seen in the course of a walk are occasional Hare and, in a few regions, deer.

In spring the uplands become more inviting. In March

the Wheatear, a small bird of the thrush family, arrives. It nests in crevices in stone walls or on banks and feeds on insects and other invertebrates caught on the ground. It is a summer visitor to the country, flying south in late autumn. The Meadow Pipit and Skylark come to the uplands from lower ground in spring and remain until the autumn. The Nightjar is a summer visitor which feeds on moths at night and nests on the ground. Birds like Meadow Pipit and Snipe which spend their entire lives in the open have brown, speckled or mottled plumage which keeps them concealed when they are resting or sitting on their eggs. In the mating season and at migration time when it is desirable for the members of a single species to keep together they need an effective way of recogniz-

Stonecrop. One of a group of plants with fleshy leaves, capable of storing water so that the plant can survive in dry, stony places.

ing members of their own species. As their plumage is of very limited value for this such birds have very distinctive songs and flight calls and the males usually sing on the wing so that they will be as conspicuous as possible.

The Kestrel is a common hawk and may be seen hovering above the ground, searching for small animals, mainly frogs and large insects. Song Thrush, Blackbird, Hedge Sparrow, Robin and Wren are found, especially where the cover, in the form of bracken or brambles, is dense. In autumn parties of Mistle Thrush wander from place to place on the hillsides, attracted by the red berries of Mountain Ash and other plants. The Ring Ouzel, a close relation of the Blackbird with similar habits, is a rather uncommon summer visitor and is confined to mountain regions. Swifts come to the hills to hunt for flying insects but their nests are normally on lower ground.

The limestone regions of the West present one of the most curious features of the country and the nearest thing to desert that we have. The rock is completely bare on the surface, even on level ground. In all other parts of the country the only rock exposed on a large scale is that in steep or vertical cliffs. Otherwise soil of some kind develops and covers them. Besides the bare rock another feature of the limestone is the absence of rivers. There is plenty of rain but it runs off the rock surface into the crevices and disappears underground. The typical centre of this type of land is the Burren region of County Clare.

Although the surface of the limestone is bare the region is extremely rich in plant life. Rich, limey soil accumulates in the crevices which criss-cross the rock and both here and in scattered open places a variety of remarkable plants thrive. The month of May is the best

Dryas. One of the most striking plants of the Burren land in Co. Clare. It is normally confined to high mountains and arctic regions.

time to see them in flower but many of the species have later flowering times. The best known of them are Dryas, the beautiful Blue Gentian, and the Hypnoid Saxifrage. The most remarkable thing about plants such as the Dryas is that they are arctic or alpine species, common as mountain flowers in cold regions but rare in mild climates such as ours. In the limestone regions these plants, far from being confined to the hills grow almost down to sea level. Other plants in the same region belong normally to the Mediterranean flora, these include the Maidenhair Fern and the Close-flowered Orchid. Besides these which are rarities over most of the country, there is a profusion of more common plants of rich country such as Bird's Foot Trefoil. In the few places where extensive soil develops there are small Hazel woods.

5 FORESTS

The Irish landscape was dominated by forest for a long period until about 300 B.C. when Neolithic Man appeared. These colonists reduced the forest area both by cutting down trees and by increasing the numbers of forest fires. Later on, about 500 B.C., the climate became wetter and the growth of peat destroyed more of the forest. The area of trees was gradually reduced until the unsettled times of the sixteenth and seventeenth centuries when landowners sold their timber on a large scale and made no attempt to replant. The tide of destruction turned in the eighteenth century when the landlords once more began to plant trees and many of our finest forests of broad-leaved trees date from that time. The Royal Dublin Society in the eighteenth century encouraged planting by presenting awards to the developers of forests. The nineteenth century saw a gradual increase in the area of woodland but the most spectacular developments have come about in the present century and are largely the results of Government investment. So the forests are mostly public property and the Forestry Division is making great efforts to ensure that they can be enjoyed as recreation areas as well as being of commercial value. Most of the trees in the forestry plantations are exotic conifers, chosen for their rapid growth and freedom from disease. The native hardwoods in general grow too slowly for economical development on a large scale.

Forest is the natural condition of practically all fertile land in Ireland. Grassland exists only because of the intensive grazing that cattle and sheep subject it to. Undergrazed land turns into scrub quite rapidly and would eventually revert to forest with such trees as Holly, Hazel, Ash and Oak among others. Most of the broad-leaved trees in Ireland are 'deciduous', shedding all of their leaves for the winter. The common coniferous trees, with the exception of the Larch, are 'evergreens'. They shed their leaves at intervals but not all at the same time so that they always show plenty of green. Evergreens cast a permanent deep shade over the ground beneath the trees and when they are well grown the floor of the forest is carpeted with brown, fallen leaves in which no other green plants can grow. Some fungi, which live on the dead leaves, thrive in these conditions. In deciduous woodland the dense shade is present only during the summer and a number of species of flowering plants such as Bluebell, Wild Garlic and Wood Anemone are able to live in association with the trees. These plants grow up and flower early in the year and have practically finished their year's growth by the time the trees come into full leaf. Ferns and mosses also thrive in the deciduous woods and provide a beautiful soft, green carpet.

Forests have an air of stability about them on account of the great ages to which the trees live. In spite of this appearance they are places of constant change. Under natural conditions individual trees sooner or later die and fall. This leaves an open space which is rapidly invaded by other plants. First the woodland plants themselves grow in the open but they are superseded in a year or two by the species from outside, most of them typical of the hedgerow which can tolerate a certain amount of shade. Some of them, like the Bramble, may live in these spaces for many years. Before very long a number of young trees develop from seeds which have fallen from the surrounding ones. The young trees grow together for

Polyporus is a fungus which grows on dead trees. The visible point shown here is the fruiting body. Most of the fungus plant consists of thread-like 'hyphae' which live within the wood.

a while but eventually a single one dominates the others and finally kills them by the shade it produces.

In forestry plantations the development of the forest from the start can be watched. In the early stages the young trees are surrounded by the local vegetation, such as Bracken, Gorse and Bramble. As the trees grow they come to dominate the local plants more and more until they kill them altogether. Depending on the kind of trees the ground plants may be completely smothered or they may come to be replaced by woodland species. The local plants manage to survive to some extent along the edges of paths or rivers or other open spaces. Throughout the life of the forest the trees are thinned periodically and in its final stage the forest may be a comparatively open area with large trees, well spaced out. Trees in forestry plantations seldom die of old age as do those in natural woodlands.

Native woodland is comparatively scarce in Ireland and Oak is the most frequent dominant tree. Locally there are woods based on Arbutus, Holly and Hazel. More common and on a larger scale are planted woods which, however, are composed to a large extent of native trees and do not differ to any great degree from the completely natural forests. A detailed study of the ground vegetation can often distinguish between them. Common native trees apart from the three named are Yew, Ash, Birch, Alder, Mountain Ash and Willow. Scots Pine was common a few thousand years ago and its roots are often found in turf but it is believed that it had become extinct in Ireland by the seventeenth century when it was reintroduced by Cromwellian settlers. Some of the most familiar trees in the country such as Horse Chestnut, Beech, Sycamore and Larch were introduced in the seventeenth and eighteenth centuries. Later still came some of the most successful forestry species like Sitka Spruce and Contorta Pine.

Most of the Irish land birds and mammals depend on ground vegetation for their food. As there are very few plants on the floors of evergreen forest they provide a rather limited fauna. Badger quite often make their sets in these woods but hunt for food in the open. Typical birds are the Goldcrest, Great Tit, Blue Tit and Coal Tit. They feed on the insects and spiders which live amongst the leaves and branches. The Chiffchaff visits these woods in summer.

The only strictly woodland mammals in Ireland are the Pine Marten and the Red and Grey Squirrels. The Pine Marten is a carnivore, closely related to the Stoat but rather larger. Its numbers fluctuate but at present it is on the increase and is found in a number of forest areas. There are thought to be less than 200 individuals. It is a shy creature which lives on birds, squirrels and smaller mammals, hunting mainly by night so that it is seldom noticed. The Red Squirrel was probably a native species but became extinct around the eighteenth century and has been re-introduced. As with the Pine Marten its numbers are variable but it is very much more common and widely distributed. The Grey Squirrel was introduced at the beginning of the present century and has become established in the north midlands. Both Squirrels build nests of twigs called 'dreys' and breed twice a year. They feed largely on nuts and seeds and may damage trees by stripping the bark.

In the older evergreen woods where the trees have been thinned so that ground plants can grow and in the deciduous forests there is much more animal life than in the dark young coniferous plantations. Most of the birds mentioned in Chapter 3 may be found in the clear-

Coniferous trees, such as the Sitka Spruce, are the most valuable timber producers in commercial forests. Sixtyfive year old specimens at Avondale, Co. Wicklow.

ings. Woodcock and Pheasant are also common. Some, like the Wood Pigeon, are especially abundant. The Tree-creeper is a specifically woodland bird which hunts for insects amongst the crevices of tree trunks. In woods where the softbarked Wellingtonia tree is found the Tree-creeper excavates a hollow in the bark to roost in. The Jay, feeding mainly on nuts and berries, is another woodland bird seldom found far from trees. Just as the ground-feeding birds and mammals are found in the open parts of forests so the forest birds are found in fairly open parkland where there are enough groups of trees to support them.

In the dark young coniferous forests few green plants besides the trees can grow. Where there are small breaks in the cover and light penetrates to the carpet of dead leaves, plants like ferns can survive.

6 WETLANDS AND BOG

The word 'wetland' is a modern one, describing assemblages of land and water more than familiar to any Irish person. It includes all marshes and stretches of water of less than twenty feet deep whether temporary or permanent. It is a useful term because such marshes and small lakes are variable things, marshes turn into lakes in wet weather and lakes into marshes in drought. It also covers a number of habitats which are treated elsewhere in this book such as rivers, some of the lakes and tidal lagoons and estuaries.

As a result of large scale drainage the areas of wetland in Ireland and all over Europe are steadily being reduced. Fortunately conservation organizations are making efforts to preserve at least some of them. Apart from the great scientific and recreational value of the wetlands certain features of them are of direct economic importance. For example they serve as natural reservoirs retaining water which may be used for drinking and industry, and they control flooding. They also serve frequently as nursery grounds for birds and fishes of importance as food animals. It even happens that land reclaimed from wetlands loses its value instead of gaining since boating and hunting visitors may contribute very much more to a local community then the extra cattle that might be raised.

In the permanent water of the wetlands the plant community is the same as by lake margins. Above the permanent open water the soil is waterlogged and Reeds, Bullrush and some Horsetails are found. Under favourable conditions the Reeds grow to six feet and more in height and make impressive forests. When dry they are often cut and used for thatching, the long straight 'straw' being especially suitable. Amongst the Reeds some trees sometimes grow, especially the Alder. In other, rather drier, swamps and by river banks the Alder is a dominant plant; and the Osier Willow is another tree capable of surviving very wet conditions. Rushes, Yellow Flag and Sedges cover large areas of marsh land, where they can survive varying conditions from growing on islets in shallow water to pastures which are only occasionally flooded. A number of striking plants are associated with the marsh but seldom dominate it. These include Ragged Robin, Marsh Marigold, Meadowsweet, Water Mint, various Buttercups, Forget-me-nots and Cotton Grass. In places some of these may dominate a few acres and provide sheets of colour when they flower.

Marshes and floodlands favour the development of certain insects with aquatic larvae which, however, are able to survive when the open water recedes and they are left in wet mud. Various species of Leather-jackets, larvae of Daddy-long-legs flies, thrive there. Other insects, especially species of flies, which can complete their life histories in a matter of weeks or months also benefit from the alternations of wet and dry conditions. Both dry-land and aquatic species can complete their cycles during the alternating dry or wet periods. Many of the insects and other animals which would normally compete with or prey on them are unable to live in these places. On the other hand aquatic insects like Mayflies and Dragonflies which require a year or more of conditions of open water cannot exist. Flying insects like water beetles and water boatmen are able to feed there during wet periods and leave in dry and some of the planktonic crustaceans can produce 'resting' eggs which survive the dry periods, to hatch when the water returns.

Turloughs are a form of wetland peculiar to Ireland. They are found in the limestone country west of the Shannon. In wet periods when the water table is high they form lakes, some as much as twenty feet deep. In dry spells the water level falls, sometimes leaving the turlough completely dry, sometimes reducing the area of water to a small pool. The water enters through springs and swallow holes and is very clear. The surrounding land is mostly fissured limestone covered with shrubs and in dry weather an empty turlough can usually be recognized by the sudden cessation of the bushes. A distinctive plant of the region is a black moss which grows around the lowest few feet of the shrub zone. The bed of the turlough is covered with a green sward of various land plants.

In addition to their exceptionally interesting plant life – which has never been fully studied – the turloughs in winter form some of the finest places for water birds. Wild geese, swans and surface-feeding duck come to some of them in enormous numbers. They have a double attraction for the wildfowl in combining the green sward for grazing with open water for a safe retreat.

Frog and Newt are both well adapted to life in the regions of small pools and marshes. The adult Frog is a land animal but must keep to fairly moist conditions. The Newt lives in the water but can survive for some time on land, again provided that it is kept moist. Both of them hibernate buried in wet mud. Their life processes in hibernation move at such a low rate that they are able to get sufficient oxygen from the surrounding water. They lay their eggs in ponds or by the margins of lakes and these hatch into fully aquatic tadpoles which die quickly if removed from the water. Frog spawn is deposited from February into late spring. Newts spawn later and since they lay their eggs singly instead of in conspicuous clusters they are far less well known. Many masses of frogspawn perish because the Frog has chosen a puddle or ditch which dries up before the eggs can hatch. On the other hand the tadpoles that hatch in the permanent water of large ponds are liable to be eaten by fishes and water beetles. In spite of the difficulties Frogs are highly successful animals in Ireland and are very widely distributed. It is not known whether they are native species or were introduced artificially.

Typical water birds are found in the wetter parts of the wetlands and land birds haunt the dry regions. A few species live in between. The sparrow-like Reed Bunting nests amongst Reeds or Alders and feeds partly on the seeds of water plants and partly on snails and insects. The Water Rail is quite common but rarely seen. It is related to Corncrake and Moorhen and spends its life amongst thick vegetation, seldom coming into the open except on migratory flights. Like so many of the inconspicuous birds it has a loud and distinctive call, rather like the squealing of a pig. In summer Sedge Warbler comes to nest. It feeds on insects and the male is often to be seen perched on Reed stems and singing its raucous, chattering song. The Grasshopper Warbler has similar habits and a song very like the noise of a grasshopper. It is rather local in distribution. The Pheasant is common in some reed swamps and nests on the ground. As in the case of the ducks and some other birds which nest in the open the male is brilliantly coloured and does not sit on the eggs. It is an introduced species which probably would not survive under natural conditions in this country, but the stocks are maintained by artificial rearing and the release of the young into the wild.

The most abundant type of soil found in Ireland has

Reed Swamp. Tall grasses thrive in swampy conditions and make excellent cover for birds.

developed as a result of wet conditions. This is peat, more commonly known as turf. Its development began following a climatic change from relatively dry to very wet about two thousand, five hundred years ago. Heavy rain and poor drainage led to the accumulation of water-logged soil and acid conditions. These favoured in particular the development of Sphagnum moss. The lack of lime and of soil aeration prevents the development and action of the bacteria that normally bring about the decay of dead plants. So the dead material accumulates and the soil grows higher and higher. The peat itself is waterlogged and no drainage takes place so the process continues.

There are two main types of turf bog in Ireland. The first is the Raised Bog which is found mainly in the centre of the country and practically nowhere south of County Tipperary. It grows up above the surrounding country and in places its steep edge some fifteen feet in height can be seen though as a rule it has been cut away over the years. Raised bog is typically dome-shaped and has an average depth of about eighteen feet. Heather is usually the dominant plant. Crossleaved Heath, Rushes, Bog Cotton and Bog Asphodel are all common and there is plenty of Sphagnum. The raised bog is typical of the central lowlands and dominates the scenery for miles around with its practically level surface.

The other type, Blanket Bog, depends for its existence on high rainfull and is confined to the west of the country and to mountains in the east. Instead of forming a great area of level ground by filling up hollows it follows the contours of the land and averages five or six feet in depth. Blanket Bog and the 'poor pasture' of Chapter 4 merge into one another where they meet. The pasture in fact is very often developed where the bog has been cut away for fuel. In many places the rainfall has become a little too low for the bog to continue its growth or even to maintain itself. In these regions of decaying bog hummocks with their covering of Heather and other plants are separated by gulleys where the rain is eating the peat away. No plants are able to grow on these unstable surfaces. Sedges and Moorland Grass give the bog of the Atlantic coast its characteristic green colour. Deer Grass in winter gives the mountain bog its brown shades. Heather dominates the drier parts and Bog Asphodel and Bog Cotton are common in places.

The higher animals of the bog are much the same as in the poor pasture but sheep and deer are very few. The bog lakes and rivers are practically all poor in minerals and therefore plant and animal life is sparse. The White Water Lily is one of the most striking members of the bog lake flora in western counties.

Turf bog is essentially an acid soil, derived from the partial decay of plants. It has a very low mineral content and an acid reaction. Fen is a different type of organic soil, being rich in minerals, especially lime. Fenland is a rather uncommon community in Ireland.

7 INLAND WATERS – RIVERS

A great deal of water falls on Ireland. The mean annual rainfall ranges from 30 inches in the east to 70 inches in the South and West. A small proportion of it evaporates but by far the greater part sinks into the soil to appear again in the open as a stream or lake, eventually running back to the sea. About one third of the country drains into the Shannon, the rest of the water leaves by smaller rivers.

A typical river starts its life as a small mountain stream, running out of a marsh. In its upper reaches it flows swiftly and descends steeply. Lower down the slope decreases and so does the speed of the water. Water in motion tends to eat away the walls that confine it. It actually dissolves solid rock and this is especially noticeable in limestone regions where caverns are formed and a considerable proportion of drainage is underground. More generally water removes solid particles and carries them along with it. Even water from the clearest imaginable mountain stream will contain small pieces of grit or particles of the roots of plants. A stream or river in flood can move substantial boulders.

The faster the water the more it can carry in the way of solids. The rapid mountain streams always have clean gravel beds. This is because the water is always moving quickly enough to carry away the small particles of soil which form mud. As soon as the gravel is disturbed it releases a cloud of mud which has lain beneath its surface, sheltered by the grit. When these streams flood they become more or less turbid partly from fresh soil worn away from the banks. Over the years rivers are continually changing their shapes and courses as the solid material is carried away. As the river goes to lower ground the speed of the water is reduced and it cannot carry solids to the same extent. So the particles are deposited and the typical lowland stream has a bed of soft mud, composed of fine particles of silt. In the same way silt is deposited at the upstream ends of lakes. As a river enters a lake its speed is reduced abruptly and the solid material accumulates in a fan-shaped area. Over the years this 'alluvial fan' as it is called tends to rise above the lake surface and eventually becomes dry land.

The plant and animal life of the waters depends partly on the physical features – mountain stream or lowland river or lake. It is also influenced by the chemicals which get dissolved as the water flows. In general where the drainage is over poor land, bog or mountain pasture, the rivers and lakes will have sparse populations of slow-growing plants and animals. When the drainage is through rich land both the quantities and variety of plants and animals in the watercourses will be greater.

The mountain streams are nearly always sparsely populated. This is mainly due to the speed of the water though the fact that in Ireland nearly all of them contain drainage water from poor land has some influence. The rushing water tends to dislodge plants and the prevalence of gravel adds to the effect because the plants are unable to root in it. So most of the plants are very small ones like algae and mosses and they grow best on the downstream sides of stones and boulders. In the occasional sheltered pools higher plants do gain a foothold. Most of them are types, like the Crowfoots which have tassels of hair-like leaves which offer very little resistance to the flow.

Insects and snails are the dominant animals. They are all small and nearly all are creeping rather than burrowing or swimming species. The River Limpet has a streamlined conical shell which the animal holds very tightly to the stones on which it lives. It feeds by grazing on the algae which form a thin layer on the stones. The freshwater molluscs spend their entire lives in the water and cannot survive out of it for long. Like fishes they breathe by extracting dissolved oxygen from the water. The insects which live in water are never entirely aquatic and all of them in their adult stages must breathe air. The majority of their larvae, however, live beneath the surface and are equipped with gills for respiration. In the upper waters the dominant insects are the stoneflies and mayflies with caddis, black flies and chironomid midges. The adults of all of these are fully terrestrial creatures which indulge in a mating flight after which the females deposit their eggs in the water. Most of them have very short adult lives during which their sole function is breeding. Exceptions are the black flies which feed by biting and sucking the blood of mammals including humans.

The mayfly and stonefly larvae in the mountain streams are all flattened, crawling insects which cling to the lower sides of the stones. Their flattened bodies offer very little resistance to the water. The blackfly larvae attach themselves to stones by their tails and hang in the water, feeding on smaller organisms which are carried by. When they pupate they build streamlined shelters firmly stuck to the stones. The caddis larvae live either in cases built of sand grains and fixed to stones or else spin small webs in crevices on the stones and hold on to these by powerful hooks at the tips of their tails. The chironomids live amongst the mosses where they are protected from the current by the leaves. These insects can easily be found by picking up stones in a stream and

Fish Fence. A fence made of netting wire to capture Salmon for research purposes. A trap at the left hand of the fence catches adult salmon going upstream. The channel at the right leads to a trap for migrating smolts and kelts. Salmon Research Trust, Newport, Co. Mayo.

looking on the undersides of them. Rough stones like granites generally have far more inhabitants than smooth ones.

The higher animals of mountains streams are few. The only fishes are small Brown Trout and Eel. They grow slowly on account of the shortage of their invertebrate prey. The typical bird of the streams is the Dipper which goes beneath the surface to hunt for insects and small fishes. The Grey Wagtail also lives by upland streams and feeds on the adult insects, caught in the air.

In the slow water of the lower reaches there is far more life. Many types of water weed are able to grow. They differ from the upstream plants in having broad leaves.

Some, such as Watercress, have weak trailing stems, others like Dropwort and Brooklime stand upright. The mud and slow water help dense vegetation to grow and the vegetation adds to its effect by further reducing the speed of flow and by adding to the mud both by trapping silt among the leaves and by decay of the dead plants. Under normal conditions these plants by their photosynthesis contribute to the amount of dissolved oxygen in the water. From time to time in very hot weather when water is low a dense growth of water weed can reduce the oxygen to a dangerously low level at night by respiration when they take in more oxygen than they give out. Fish are sometimes killed by this.

As far as the animal inhabitants of fresh water are concerned the higher plants are of far greater importance as shelters and supports than as food. Most of the animals eat either smaller animals or microscopic plants which are attached to the surfaces of the larger plants. Crawling animals are found in the lower reaches, typical ones being the Water Lice, closely allied to the Woodlice. Their bodies are flattened but not to the same extent as the upstream insects and they are scarce in swift waters. Swimming and burrowing invertebrates are in general far more plentiful and varied than the crawlers. Mayflies are represented by groups with more or less cylindrical bodies. Stoneflies are less plentiful than in fast water. Most of the caddis larvae have bulky cases made of coarse sand grains or of chopped up leaves and grasses. The molluscs are larger and less streamlined than the River Limpet, most of them having typical coiled snail-like shells. In the mud many kinds of worms and the larvae of chironomids and other flies live. Water beetles and water boatmen which swim actively are plentiful. They are amongst the few adult insects which live in the water and have to swim to the surface to take a supply of air for the next dive. Nearly all of them are able to leave the water and fly away.

All of the freshwater fishes of Ireland are carnivorous to a large extent. Some feed on invertebrates all their lives, others regularly take other fish as soon as they grow big enough. Pike adopt a fish diet when they are less than a year old. Trout and Perch usually wait until they are about two and sometimes apparently keep to invertebrates throughout their lives. Eels are usually at least ten before they are big enough to catch other fish. In all of these species cannibalism is normal. The Cyprinid fish, Rudd, Bream, Carp, Roach, Tench, Gudgeon and Minnow, normally eat invertebrates throughout their lives and take a fair proportion of small plant material. Wherever food is abundant and the water pure fish thrive. In the past Salmon, Trout (including Sea Trout), Eel, Stickleback and Lamprey were the only species in the Irish Rivers. In historical times, probably since the Anglo-Norman invasion, Pike, Perch and the Cyprinids were introduced. Conditions in the rich lowland rivers are far more suitable for the latter fish than for the Salmon and Trout and in the river systems to which they have been introduced Pike, Perch and some of the others have become the dominant species. These 'coarse' fish do not thrive in the poor western rivers or in the mountain streams and these are the places where Salmon and Trout predominate under natural conditions. Salmon and Sea Trout are the only fish in the poor rivers which consistently reach a large size. This is because they spend only the first one or two years of their lives in the rivers, subsequently migrating to the sea where food is abundant and growth fast. They return to the fresh waters as adults to breed but not to feed. Occasionally large Brown Trout are found in the poor waters. These are exceptionally vigorous individuals which grow quickly at the start and adopt a diet of other fish at an early stage. Trout like these are bound to be scarce because the total production of food in the poor regions is too low to support a large population of them. No amount of selective breeding could improve the situation.

Eel are found in practically all of the rivers. They breed in the Sargasso sea and their larvae take two or three years to drift across the Atlantic to our shores. In the offshore waters the larvae turn into needle-shaped 'elvers' which come up the rivers in spring and early summer. In the rivers they settle down and grow slowly until sexual maturity is reached, an event which usually takes at least ten years and may take as many as forty. The mature eels migrate downstream in autumn on their way back to the Sargasso to breed and die. There are important commercial fisheries for them on some of the larger rivers.

The Stickleback is another very widely distributed fish in fresh water (it can also live in salt) and has very interesting breeding habits. It is the only freshwater fish in Ireland which builds a nest and takes care of its young. The male builds the nest, a barrel-shaped structure, and entices a succession of females to go in and lay their eggs. He then guards nest and eggs and keeps the young together until they are old enough to look after themselves.

Lampreys are quite common but not very often seen. There are three species. All three have a long larval life which they spend in the mud, feeding on small organisms. The adults of two of them go to sea and lead a parasitic life, burrowing into larger fishes including Salmon; the third never feeds as an adult.

All the three species breed in freshwater.

Pike lead solitary lives, feeding on other fish which they capture by lying in wait until one passes close enough and then pouncing out. The other coarse fish live in shoals.

Most of the birds of the lowland rivers are at least as common on lakes and ponds and will be treated in the next section. The Kingfisher is more of a river than a lake bird and favours slow lowland streams and canals with plenty of overhanging bushes. It perches a few feet above the water and dives in for fish or insects. The water must be relatively clear so that the bird can see its prey beneath the surface.

In spite of being trapped and shot in the interests of salmon conservation the Otter is still a reasonably common animal. While it will hunt in lakes and in the sea rivers are its normal habitat. Rapid rivers with large clear pools where salmon and other fish may congregate offer the best conditions. It is generally believed by the owners of salmon fisheries that the Otter is a pest but there is no real evidence available one way or the other. The damage done by the Otter in eating salmon is obvious. On the positive side are the facts that it eats fish such as Brown Trout which can do considerable harm in a salmon river and that sometimes salmon waters are actually over-stocked with spawning fish. In the absence of positive proof in either direction it might be wiser to give the Otter the benefit of the doubt.

Rats are often plentiful by river banks, especially in the suburbs and near farms where waste food is thrown in. They can swim well both on the surface and under water. There is no Water Rat in Ireland. The Bank Vole was first discovered in 1964 and may be found in Kerry and Limerick.

8 INLAND WATERS – STILL WATERS

Ponds, reservoirs, lakes and canals provide an extension of the freshwater community. The water in them is relatively still. It seldom flows in strong currents except where rivers enter or leave. The action of the wind causes wave movement so that there is a certain amount of erosion of materials along the shore lines. The most marked effect of water movement is the rise and fall of the lake surface resulting from wet or dry periods. This may add greatly to the area of dry land exposed and reduces the numbers of invertebrates that can live close to the shore. The more active swimmers like water-boatmen can escape but many of the creeping types, like snails, are left stranded. Some of the higher plants that grow by the lake margins can tolerate the alternating conditions. Others, like Reed and Bullrush are less adaptable and usually grow a short way out from the shore line where they are not likely to be left dry.

The abundance of plants and animals in the lakes depends partly on the chemistry of the water, especially the quantity of lime in solution. The Connemara lakes, where the water is deficient in lime, have sparse populations and the invertebrates are nearly all very small species. The midland lakes are typical of the rich type and have a dense growth of plants which in turn support a large and varied animal population. The other important factor controlling the life in a lake is its depth and the profile of its bed. Production depends directly on the amount of light so it is at its highest in the top few feet of water. In deeper water less light penetrates and fewer plants can develop. So a lake which has a uniform bed a few feet deep and rich water will be highly productive. One with the same chemical make-up in its water but which plunges rapidly will be much poorer because the productive zone is limited to a few yards around the margin. If the water is deficient in lime the lake will be a poor one anyway but it, too, will have its greatest production in the shallow parts.

In the poor lakes reeds grow sparsely in the shallows and various Pondweeds with broad leaves spread over a considerable area. In the west the White Water-lily is a very striking and beautiful feature. It is unusual in such waters in having very large flowers. The invertebrates are in general an impoverished cross-section of the groups found in the rich waters. The common fishes are Brown Trout, Sea Trout, Eel and Stickleback. Perch, Pike and the Cyprinids seldom thrive in these waters. An extremely interesting fish is found scattered through some of the poor lakes. This is the Char, a relative of salmon and trout. It is properly an arctic or sub-arctic species and closely related ones are found in northern Europe and America where they are the dominant fresh-water fish. After the Glaciation but before the climate reached its present mildness the Char must have been plentiful in the Irish lakes. As conditions grew warmer they became more suitable for Brown Trout and Salmon and these gradually ousted the Char. With the exception of Lough Corrib the Char is now confined to isolated poor lakes.

As in the upland pastures birds are scarce in the poor lakes. Moorhen, Mallard and Teal sometimes live in them or close by. On some islands there are colonies of Black-headed Gulls but they use the lakes more as safe nesting places rather than as feeding grounds and they forage over a much wider area. In one or two

Lake Island. A small island on Lough Corrib where Common Gulls and various species of duck breed and completely natural plant life is found.

places in County Donegal the Red-throated Diver nests on lake islands. As with the gulls it does not use the lakes as a feeding ground but flies off to sea to hunt. It is very much a water bird and cannot move efficiently on land so that it must build its nest close to the water's edge. This is impossible in tidal water so the Diver has to come inland.

The poor lakes have the advantage that there are few plant and animal species and they are therefore relatively easy to study. The rich ones are very much more lively but more complicated. In general the shallower the water the denser the weed, provided that the normal rise and fall of the lake does not leave the weed dry. Wherever there is a reasonable degree of shelter from wind and waves a bed of upstanding plants develops. These may be Reed, Bullrush or several types of rushes or sedges. They often grow to a height of five or six feet and in many lakes form a dense fringe close to the water's edge. They are mostly perennials which grow up each year from submerged roots. The dead stems and leaves often persist through the winter. In deeper water the bed of the lake is carpeted with various kinds of plants such as Mare's Tail and Canadian Pondweed whose tips just reach to the surface at the peak of their growth. As the depth increases the plants decrease. They are represented by Pondweeds which have submerged or floating leaves and extremely long, trailing stems. An interesting variation on the theme is the Water Lobelia which has a rosette of leaves on the bottom and sends its flowers to bloom at the surface at the tips of slender stems which may reach a length of six feet or more. In depths of over six feet the plants which extend to the surface become very scarce and the bed is covered in places by lower plants such as charophytes and algae.

Reed beds are at their best in small lakes or in small bays of large ones where there is little erosion from wave action. The large lakes have rather barren margins in this respect. Heavy weed growth is regarded as a nuisance by owners of fish ponds who wish to be able to fish from the banks. The only treatment is annual cutting or uprooting of the weeds and it is usually simpler to take a boat or build fishing stands which run out through the weed bed and into deeper water.

As in the case of the slow rivers the larger water weeds are of greater importance to the animals as supports and shelter than as fodder. They also serve to supply much of the oxygen. The basic plant food on which all of the animals ultimately depend comes mainly in the form of algae both attached to the bed and to other plants and in the form of drifting microscopic plants. From time to time there is a particularly rich bloom of these plants and the surface waters of the lake become tinted with green or blue-green. The green algae in general cause no trouble but occasionally an upsurge of blue-green species occurs which may produce toxic substances or cause serious depletion of oxygen leading to the death of fish and some of the invertebrates in places. A protracted spell of hot, calm weather provides suitable conditions for such a bloom. Most of the invertebrates of the slow rivers are found in the shallower parts of lakes and the same is true of the fishes. In the deeper parts animal life is very much scarcer. Another Glacial relict fish lives in Loughs Erne, Derg and Neagh. This is the Pollan, known in other countries as Whitefish. It looks very like a Herring but is in fact a member of the Salmon family. As it feeds entirely on very small invertebrates, most of them planktonic forms, it is rarely caught by anglers but the Lough Neagh Pollan are caught by nets early in summer and sold in Belfast.

In winter and summer birds are abundant on the rich lakes. Some, like Swift, Swallow and Sand and House Martin are purely dining visitors, flying over the water to catch the insects which emerge from underwater larval stages. The others shelter, feed and often nest in or about the lake. The shallow lakes have relatively much larger populations of water birds than the deep ones since the birds depend for their food on the plants or animals which abound in shallow water. Usually the only birds which swim over deep parts are those which have been disturbed from the shallows and are waiting until it is safe to return there.

The birds which are most strongly dependent on still waters are those like the Dabchick, the Coot, the Tufted

Duck and the Mute Swan which may spend their entire lives in the fresh water. The Dabchick dives and chases fish and insects under water. The Tufted Duck also dives and swims under water but usually feeds on invertebrates and weed which it finds on the bottom. The Coot is another diver: it lives mainly on water weed. The Swan eats water weed but finds it simply by stretching its long neck down and not swimming under water. The Dabchick builds a floating nest of stems of water weeds amongst the reeds. The Coot's nest is also surrounded by water but is firmly attached to the stems of reeds while the Tufted Duck and Swan nest on dry land, but always close to the water's edge.

Moorhen, Mallard and Teal are typical of the next grade of water birds. They nest close to the water and their chicks or ducklings find their food there. The adults also feed on the water, often taking shallow dives but they regularly leave it to hunt for food in marshes or on dry land. The Great Crested Grebe and the Red-

Diving Duck. Tufted Duck which live on food caught on the bottom in shallow water. In the background is a Coot, another diving bird of shallow lakes and large ponds.

breasted Merganser come to the lakes for the summer. The Grebe, like the Dabchick builds a floating nest, the Merganser nests on dry land, usually choosing a small island. Both of them chase fish below the surface and as a rule leave the lakes and go to coastal waters for the winter. The Cormorant sometimes nests inland, usually in a tree, and regularly feeds in lakes and large rivers but it is more common as a seabird in this country.

Common Tern, Black-headed Gull and Common Gull nest on lake islands, the Black-headed Gull also nests in wet marshes and all three breed on the coast as well. The Tern is strictly a summer visitor and is confined to the water. It feeds on insects and small fish which it captures by flying above the surface and taking very shallow dives. The two gulls also use these tactics but their range is more extensive and they can feed on dry land where they are often seen following the plough in search of insects. The Common Gull breeds in the north and west of the country, the other two are more widely distributed.

On the shore a number of wading birds breed. The Common Sandpiper is the commonest. Redshank and Ringed Plover are less plentiful. The three make open but very well camouflaged nests on the ground. The nests in fact are little more than scratches in the gravel or amongst stones and the eggs are cryptically coloured. They feed on insects and other invertebrates caught on the lake shores. The Heron also wades but its feeding tactics are quite different. The first three search for their food in the mud or chase creatures they see on the ground. The Heron stands still and waits for a fish, frog or insect to appear and spears it suddenly; it seldom stalks or chases its prey. The Heron builds a bulky and conspicuous nest high in a tree. It is a colonial breeder and there are usually several nests in the one group of trees.

In winter the population of lake birds is greatly increased. The residents which nested in the summer stay in the country to a great extent and many more of the same species come from breeding places in the north. Wigeon which feed in the shallows like Mallard and Teal, and Pochard which have diving habits like the Tufted Duck, are the most numerous. Two species of swans, the Whooper and the Bewick's and one goose, the White-fronted are found on some lakes. The Grey-lag Goose was once common but is now a very scarce and local visitor. A number of wading birds, especially Curlew, Lapwing and Golden Plover come to feed on the lake shores.

Young dragonflies live in freshwater for one or two years before developing wings and living above the surface as adult insects. This type of life-history is typical of most of the insects which live in water.

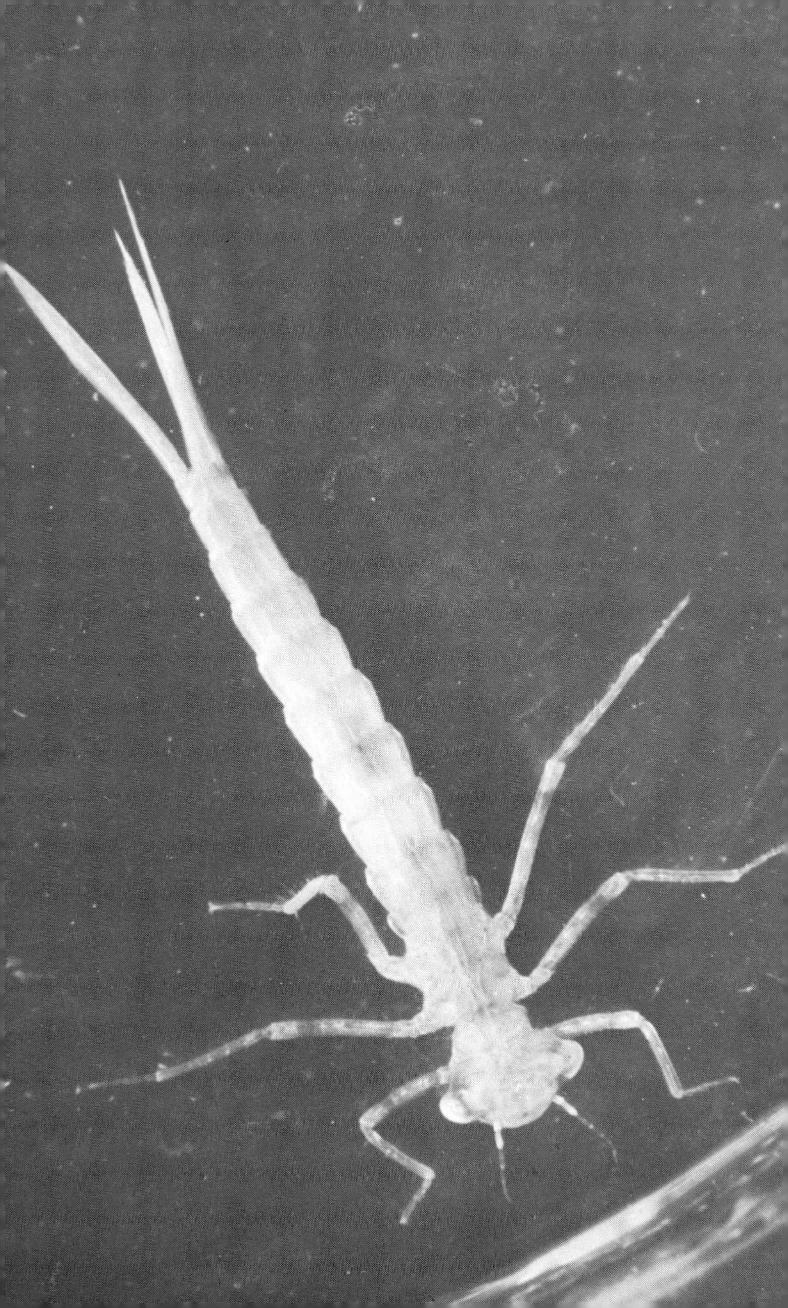

9 COAST AND SEA

(I) *Sand and rockpools*

As the song says: 'Thank God we're surrounded by water'. The sea provides a marvellously varied habitat with the added attraction that it is not too easy for Man to alter it. It certainly provides the least artificial conditions in the country. Unfortunately even the apparently boundless oceans are not completely immune from pollution. Residues of pesticides are already present and may sooner or later reach dangerous concentrations. On a smaller scale there are areas of sea where much of the natural plant and animal life has been seriously harmed by waste materials from cities. Dublin Bay no longer contains anything like pure sea water and other bays and estuaries are polluted to some extent.

The various types of coast depend for their formation on the direction of marine currents, the degree of shelter, the rock formation and the size of nearby rivers. Sandy beaches are found in exposed places where wave action prevents the accumulation of mud. They are usually in the course of building up and are good places to look for cast up shells. Shingle beaches on the other hand are typical of regions where the sea is removing material, the stones representing heavy material which is not so easily shifted as the sand. From the point of view of plants and animals these are the most barren. Rocky shores represent the end product of the erosion of soft material by waves and currents. Eventually even these are eaten away. Mud accumulates in sheltered places. It is most common in river estuaries where most of it has been carried down by the river. It also occurs in more or less land-locked bays where it builds up from the remains of dead plants and animals.

Ideal though they are for bathing sandy shores have relatively little to offer in the way of animals and shingle beaches have less. The plant communities are interesting and many species are present which are virtually unknown away from the coast. Sea Holly, Yellow Horned Poppy and Sea Campion grow a little way above the highest high tide mark. The first two have blue-green leaves with a waxy covering to reduce evaporation. Fresh water, which is required by the higher plants, is scarce in the gravel.

The dominant plant in sand dunes is Marram Grass. It is well able to stand up to the dry conditions of the shifting sand and its roots serve to bind the sand together. As soon as the Marram is well established the sand is held firmly and other plants are able to come in. These include a variety of grasses and Bird's Foot Trefoil, Rest Harrow, Sand Pansy and later on Creeping Willow. Sand dunes and the land beside them represent an expanding area of land. The sand which has been thrown up by the sea stays in position and the sea gradually recedes.

As the sand on the foreshores is constantly shifting it is rather inhospitable to small animals. A few species live there in temporary burrows. The Sandhopper is a small crustacean about half an inch in length which hides by day but comes out at dusk to hunt for food when the tide is out. Sometimes enormous swarms of them may be seen moving up and down the shore, scurrying over the sand. The line of seaweed left by spring tides is quite productive. It remains untouched by the sea for long enough to allow a number of species of flies to complete their life cycle in the two weeks between successive high

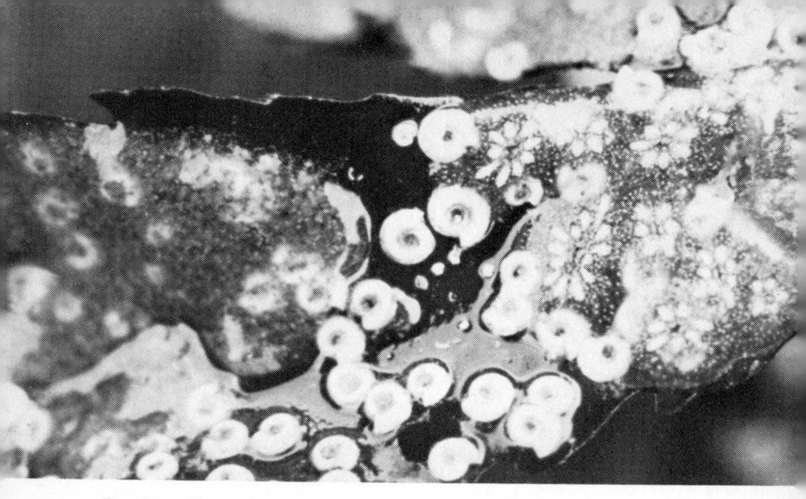

Fouling Organisms attached to a piece of seaweed about an inch in length. The star-shaped creatures are groups of Sea Squirts, the snail-like shells are made by Spirorbis Worms.

tides. A number of small birds feed on the flies and sand-hoppers. The Pied Wagtail and Ringed Plover are present throughout the year. The Wheatear comes for the summer. Meadow Pipit and Rock Pipit are common in places through the year and the Snow Bunting is sometimes seen in winter, especially in the north. In well established dunes Rabbit and Hare are important grazing animals. The Wheatear is found there as well as on the shore and Skylark and Meadow Pipit are common.

In summer Oyster Catcher and Ringed Plover nest on the shingle. On some coasts, especially Wicklow and Wexford they are joined by the Little Tern. All three do very little in the way of bringing nesting material and they lay eggs which are extremely difficult to pick out from the surrounding stones and sand. Even the black and white patterns that serve to make the adult birds so distinctive when they move serve to break up their outlines and make them inconspicuous as long as they sit still. In a few places round the coast very large colonies of terns breed on sandy or low-lying rocky shores. There are four species besides the Little Tern, namely the Common, the Arctic, the Sandwich and the Roseate. All five are coastal birds which live on small fish caught close to the surface. They are extremely graceful in flight and hunt for their prey by hovering a few feet above the surface, plunging as soon as they spot a fish. In autumn they move slowly down the coast of Europe to the Mediterranean and further, many going far south of the Equator. From the shore various gulls, Cormorant and Shag and sometimes Gannet may all be seen but they prefer rocky places for nesting.

The rocky shores teem with plant and animal life in summer. In winter they are comparatively deserted because so many of their inhabitants come inshore simply to breed and spend their first few weeks or months of life. There are two communities to consider. The first is found around the rocks and their seaweed, the second the cliffs which stand out of reach of the waves.

Life on the shore is a curious compromise between water and dry land and the animals and plants that live there have to be able to survive the abrupt change from one to another as often as twice a day. The extent of the tide varies throughout the month and to a lesser extent through the year. The highest high and lowest low tides are the spring tides which occur at New Moon and Full Moon. In between them are the neap tides in which the lower parts of the shore remain covered by water and the higher parts are dry. The strongest tides in the year take place in March and September at the equinoxes. On the upper parts of the shore where the tide seldom reaches land plants manage to survive. Lower down there are typical tidal ones, most of them types like the Bladder Wrack which are brown in colour and have air bladders in their leaves to buoy them up when the tide rises. At the lowest spring tide level Strap Wrack grows and beds of it are exposed twice a month. Below this in the permanent water red algae are the dominant plants. The rock pools, which are permanently full of sea water in spite of being regularly left above the receding tide, often have a growth of red algae. These are a beautiful pink colour and are known as Corallines.

Living things find it very difficult to survive on the highest rock of the shore. The pounding of the waves, often carrying particles of sand, tends to wear everything away. In spite of this the rocks are usually coated with a mass of encrusting plants, various species of lichens. Most of them are coloured shades of blue-green and yellow. Limpets and Barnacle are able to live on some of the most exposed rocks. The Limpet is a mollusc which grazes on the lichens and on algae with the aid of its rasp-like tongue. The main muscle of its body forms an effective sucking disc which it uses to hold its shell fast to the rock. At low tide this serves to keep the limpet moist inside its shell and in stormy weather prevents it from being swept away. It also protects it from birds. The Barnacle is a crustacean and its shell is composed of a number of plates which are cemented to the rock. The opening is at the tip and is kept closed at low water. When the tide rises the Barnacle extends its hairy arms through the opening and uses them to capture passing planktonic animals. These more or less stationary shore animals usually lay enormous numbers of eggs which hatch into active, swimming larvae. The larvae are carried about by the tide currents for some time before settling down and growing to maturity. The great majority of them die, usually getting eaten, before they find a suitable settling place but the large numbers produced ensure that every possible niche on the shore has some suitable animal to fill it.

Various species of Winkle live between the tides. They are also subject to the same risks of dehydration and being swept away that the Limpet and Barnacle face but they meet them in a different way. The Winkle can withdraw into its coiled shell and close the opening with a horny pad to keep the moisture in. It does not attempt to cling on to the rocks in rough weather but falls off and survives the battering by having a thick, tough shell. The young and more delicate Winkles keep sheltered inside empty barnacle shells or in narrow crevices in the rock. Most of the other inter-tidal animals on the rocky coasts shelter beneath fronds of seaweed when the tide is out. The weed keeps them hidden from birds and also keeps them damp. They are all capable of living and moving in the open air for at least a few minutes and often for considerably longer. Even some fishes are able to live out of the water for a while. The little eel-like Butterfish has a very slimy skin which reduces water loss.

The rock pools contain a permanent underwater flora and fauna but all of them are species which can avoid being swept away in rough weather. In this they differ from the typical inhabitants of the sea bottom which are never disturbed by the action of waves. Many of the fishes have sucking discs on their bellies which enable them to cling to rocks or weed. They also have apparently striking colour patterns and very uneven outlines which serve to disguise them amongst the weed. The shrimps can shelter amongst dense weed and so can the

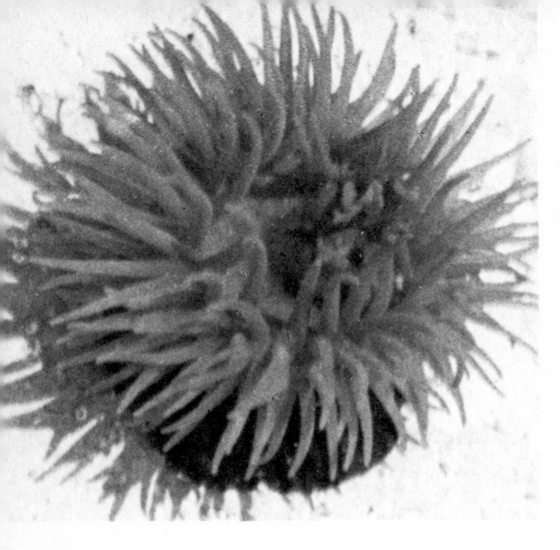

Beadlet Anemone. A very common sea-shore animal, found on rocky coasts. It can withdraw its tentacles to turn itself into a cushion-shaped creature, capable of withstanding heavy wave action.

fishes which are not supplied with suckers. The Brittle Starfish is able to survive the loss of one or more of its arms. As the arms are long and delicate this adaptation is essential. The brightly coloured sea anemones are firmly attached to the rock and their soft bodies give way to the buffeting.

In the deeper water conditions are much more stable than in the shallows or indeed on dry land. The plants and animals that live there are not subjected to changing winds or alternating rainy and dry periods. The temperature changes over long seasons, not abruptly, and with no difference between day and night. These regions are virtually closed to the general public. Their only visitors are skin divers. However, many of the fish that live there are well known as are such delectable crustaceans as Lobster, Crab and Crawfish. Pollack and Conger are common around the rocks and so are the brilliantly coloured Wrasses. The Pollack is a streamlined, fast-swimming fish. The Conger lies in wait in holes or crevices and lunges out at passing fish. The Wrasses are short

Top Shell. A sea-shore animal, living in the lower tidal zone. It has a tough shell so that it can be knocked off its hold and thrown about by the waves without coming to harm.

and deep-bodied, a shape which is associated with slow swimming and hunting for more or less stationary food. Most of them have very strong teeth and they are able to feed on shell-fish and other tough-skinned creatures.

(II) Cliffs

Steep cliffs have quite a different type of population. Flowering plants are well able to survive although the lack of soil means that they must be capable of living on a minimum of water. The beautiful Sea Pink is the most characteristic but there are many others such as Sea Campion, Sea Beet, Golden Samphire and various grasses. The great advantage that all of these plants enjoy over the inland ones is the fact that very few grazing animals are able to feed on the cliffs. This advantage is shared by the nesting seabirds which provide one of the most spectacular sights in Irish wildlife.

Some of the inhabitants of the bird cliffs are residents

in the country, staying here the whole year round. They are the Herring Gull, the Great Black-backed Gull, the Shag and the Cormorant. Shag and Cormorant are exclusively water birds. They feed on fish which they spot from the surface, diving and chasing them underwater as soon as they are seen. The Gannet is extremely local, nesting on only three southern islands. It is a magnificent bird in all respects combining large size and snowy white plumage with remarkable feeding habits. It flies above the water at a height of up to seventy feet. As soon as it spots its prey it closes its wings and plummets down to capture it. The Rock Dove and the Chough are both land birds but they are seldom seen away from marine cliffs where they nest. The Raven also nests on sea cliffs but is quite common on cliffs inland and sometimes nests in trees. The three landbirds mentioned usually make isolated nests but the seabirds are all colonial breeders.

The rest are very strictly sea or ocean birds which come to land only to nest or very occasionally when driven by severe storms. The commonest are the Kittiwake, the Razorbill and the Guillemot. The Kittiwake is a small gull, the other two are auks and look like small penguins but differ from them in being well able to fly. The first bird to be called a 'penguin' was in fact the Great Auk which was quite common in winter around the Irish coast before it became extinct in the nineteenth century. It was a flightless species but related to the other auks and having no connection with the true penguins of the Southern Hemisphere. The auks are fish eaters which hunt by swimming and diving like the Cormorant.

Two other common cliff birds are the Fulmar and the Black Guillemot but they are not so plentiful as the first three. The Fulmar is a petrel, a type of bird which flies or glides close to the surface of the ocean and feeds on floating material or on creatures which swim just below the surface. One other gull, the Lesser Black-back, is a summer visitor but otherwise has habits very similar to the Herring Gull.

None of these seabirds make any attempt to conceal their nests or eggs. The gulls, the Fulmar, Cormorant, Shag and Gannet make nests of heaps of weed and grasses. The auks lay their single eggs on the bare rock. They are distinctly pearshaped which reduces the tendency to roll off the ledges. All of the young are covered with thick down from the time they hatch and are very active, capable of walking and swimming at an early stage. The Herring and Black-backed Gull chicks usually leave the nest soon after they have hatched and hide in the vegetation nearby. The others remain in the nests or very close to them until they are ready to fly and leave them permanently.

Some of the most interesting birds of the open sea nest locally around the coast. These are the Puffin, the Shearwater and the Storm Petrel. The Puffin is an auk, Shearwater and Storm Petrel belong to groups of birds which fly just above the surface and cover immense distances in the course of the year. Puffin and Shearwater nest in burrows, either rabbit burrows or holes which they dig for themselves. Storm Petrels nest between the stones in screes or in stone walls. During the breeding season Puffins come and go all day long but the Shearwater and Storm Petrel stay away from the land all day and return to the nests at night.The parents take it in turn to sit on the eggs and sometimes, especially on bright moonlit nights, spend several days at a time on the nest. The nocturnal habits are caused by the birds' weakness on land. They cannot take off without a long

Fulmar. An ocean bird which has established itself in Ireland as a common cliff-nesting species since the turn of the century.

run and any that show themselves are liable to be caught and eaten by the large gulls.

After the breeding season the birds leave the cliffs, which have served merely as nesting sites and have practically nothing to supply in the way of food. As far as the swimming and diving ocean birds are concerned the cliffs are important not only as refuges from man and four-footed animals which might take the eggs but also as launching pads. The swimming birds have their legs set far back on the body and they are not very good at running and taking off from the land. The high nesting places mean that they can take to the air by a downward flight which is much more easily achieved.

(III) *Mud flats and salt marsh*

Muddy shores are relatively stable places. As a rule the mud is accumulating slowly and it may eventually appear permanently above the level of neap tides as salt marsh. Its level can continue to rise as plants grow and die on it without having their remains carried away so that eventually dry land is formed. The process is something of a see-saw one. The land may build up for some time but it is always liable to be swept away again by unusually strong tides and storms or by heavy flooding in river estuaries, after which it may begin to rise again. A succession of plants colonise the new land, depending on how low down the shore it is. Green algae dominate the parts still beneath the neap tide level, where the tide always covers the ground for a while. A little further up Glassworts and Eel grass are able to grow and these are the first of the land plants. Unlike normal land plants they are able to absorb water from the sea. The growth of these pioneer plants helps to accumulate mud and eventually the ground rises and they are superseded by plants which need somewhat drier conditions. In places the Ricegrass, which has great powers of binding the mud and developing dry land has been introduced to prevent erosion. Higher up the shore in the salt marsh where firm ground alternates with tidal pools and gulleys there are many more plants including Sea Lavender, Sea Aster and several rushes and grasses.

The tidal mud is a hiding or dwelling place for many invertebrates, especially worms. Some of them live permanently beneath the surface of the mud, swallowing large quantities of it and digesting the organic remains, passing the indigestible matter out at the tail end, often in the form of conical heaps of 'castings' above the surface. Other inhabitants are burrowing molluscs such as the Cockle. Then there are crabs and other crustaceans which hide in the mud or under weed at low tide and run or crawl or wriggle along the bottom when the water comes back again.

These conditions form an extremely rich feeding ground for birds and fishes. Small fishes come in search of the invertebrates. Some of them are the young of large species, certain Wrasses and various others. The rest are permanently small species, at least in Irish waters. They include various Gobies, Blennies, Sea Snails and Pipefish. The Pipefish have interesting breeding habits: the male carries the eggs and sometimes the young in a special pouch or stuck to the underside of his body. The majority of fishes lay their eggs and take no further care of the young. But many of the small species which live in estuaries and other places where there are strong currents build nests or carry their eggs with them. This makes sure that the young have a good chance of remaining close to the shore and not getting carried away to sea. Larger fish come to catch both the small fish and the larger invertebrates. The Flounder, which can live in fresh water as well as salt is the commonest flatfish but many others, including Plaice and Sole are also found. In southern parts of the country Bass and Grey Mullet are common. Brown Trout, Sea Trout and Eel are found in most estuaries and Shad and Scad in a few. In summer the various species of Terns haunt the estuaries and bays in search of the small fish. Gulls also congregate where there are large shoals of fish but they lack the expertise of the Terns in catching them.

At the end of the summer many of the fish retire to deeper water. The Terns leave and the fish-eating birds are limited to rather small numbers of diving species such as Great Northern and Red-throated Divers which nest in countries to the north and Merganser and Great Crested Grebe which come from their inland breeding grounds. Cormorant and Shag are also present and there are a number of scarcer species such as the Long-tailed Duck. Small numbers of Heron fish in the pools or along the margins of the water.

In winter these muddy areas are transformed by the arrival of enormous numbers of birds. Some of them, the gulls for example, are resident species which simply move across from their breeding grounds. Small numbers of many of the dominant species also breed here but the great majority come from widely scattered nesting places in the far north. The Shelduck is one of the most striking of the residents. It nests in a burrow close to the shore and in summer family parties of ducklings in charge of both parents may be seen. Shelduck differ from ordinary duck in having no plumage difference between male and female. Both are conspicuous black and white birds; as they nest below ground there is no need for the duck to wear cryptic colours. In winter the numbers of Shelduck are greatly increassed by visitors.

Wigeon and Pintail are the most numerous duck but many other species including Mallard, Teal and Shoveller are common. They are 'dabbling' duck which feed on plants and invertebrates which they find on the shore or in shallow water. They keep to the shallows unless they get disturbed in which case they fly out and settle in deep water. In some sheltered bays diving duck like Scoter, Scaup and Goldeneye are plentiful. They dive beneath the surface and feed on shellfish and worms which they find on the bottom.

The most abundant birds, however, are the wading types. Most of them have long legs and long bills. They wade in the shallows or patter about on the mud, searching for buried invertebrates by probing with their bills. Others have shorter legs and bills and are more inclined to run after creatures on the surface or to hunt by turning over pieces of seaweed. Nearly all of them have similar colour patterns, shades of mottled brown or grey above and whitish beneath. In flight they show contrasting patterns of brown and white, each species having a distinctive pattern Convenient for bird-watchers who are trying to identify them these patterns are essential for the birds, enabling them to pick out other members of their own species and keep to their own flock. A small number of the shore birds instead of the pale brown colour patterns have contrasting black and white plumage. The outstanding example is the Oystercatcher, and the Lapwing gives a similar impression.

Two species of seals are common around the coast and breed on our shores. Both give birth to their young

Pintail. The most numerous species of duck in the world, common in Ireland as a winter visitor.

on land and come out of the water to bask on the shore. The Common or Harbour Seal breeds in June and gives birth either in the sea or on land exposed by the tide. The pup can swim from birth. The Grey Seal breeds in October in colonies on a number of islands around the coast.

Finally something must be said of the inhabitants of the open sea. Most of the higher animals there are the fishes and they are seldom seen until caught. They are divided into classes by their habits: the pelagic and the demersal. Pelagic fish are those like Herring, Mackerel, Porbeagle and Basking Shark which are found close to the surface at least for substantial parts of their adult lives. The demersal ones normally live near the bottom or on it and include the flatfish and most of the 'white' fish such as Cod, Whiting and Haddock. To complicate matters the young of most of the demersal fish lead a pelagic life.

The largest creatures living in the sea are the cetaceans and they are mammals, not fishes. They are warm-blooded and must come to the surface to breathe in air. Many species have been reported around our coasts from time to time but few of them are very common. The Porpoise is the most familiar of them. It is relatively small, seldom more than six feet or so in length and its back may be seen breaking the surface again and again but it seldom leaps clear. The Common Dolphin is larger and scarcer and makes spectacular leaps in the air. The Pilot Whale is the commonest whale and a few are stranded in most years.

In recent years 'sea watching' for birds has become a popular study. Besides the native cliff-nesting seabirds a number of oceanic species which never come to our shores may be seen. Nearly every year an Albatross is reported, sometimes more than one. Great Shearwater and Cory's Shearwater are seen regularly, sometimes in large numbers. These birds breed in the Southern Hemisphere and wander northwards in their winter so they appear as summer visitors in our latitudes. The Balearic Shearwater is another reasonably common type. It nests in the Mediterranean and comes as far as Ireland to feed between sessions on the eggs. Several species of skua may be seen in spring and autumn. They are parasitic birds which chase gulls and terns, frightening them so that they throw up their latest meals which the skuas then eat.

With the open sea we reach the end of our general description of the wild life of Ireland. The next section is taken county by county and selects for each one the places of outstanding interest. As far as possible the order of treatment in each county follows the order of the topics covered in the general chapters. Beginning with Dublin the coastal counties are described in order. The inland counties follow beginning with Fermanagh and following a zig-zag line to Tipperary.

10 THE COASTAL COUNTIES

Dublin

The county of Dublin is dominated by people and built-up areas. In spite of its comparatively small area it provides a remarkable variety of communities. The extreme result of human activity is seen in the lower reaches of the River Tolka S13 where the water is so heavily polluted that practically no animal life can survive. It can be traced upstream past the main source of pollution at Finglas to where it is a clear and rather rich stream.

In the centre of the city O'Connell Street in winter has a spectacular bird roosting place in the Plane trees which line the centre of the street. Very large numbers of Starling and several hundred Pied Wagtail gather there at dusk every night. St Stephen's Green offers almost everything that can be desired in the way of a city park. The ponds are tenanted by Herring Gull, Mallard and Moorhen and the shrubs support many of the smaller birds, including the Goldcrest in winter. There and also in the Dublin Zoo these birds are exceptionally tame and easy to watch. Phoenix Park offers magnificent open spaces within easy reach of the city centre. Fallow Deer, Fox, Otter, Rabbit and Red Squirrel may be found and Jay and Hooded Crow are common. The effect of grazing by deer and cattle can be seen on the trees in the open which are devoid of branches up to about six feet above the ground. The difference between them and the ungrazed woods in enclosures is very striking.

The River Liffey runs roughly from east to west. Downstream it is tidal and rather heavily polluted, in spite of which Salmon and Eel are able to pass safely through to cleaner parts. Upstream of Palmerston O03 it is a typical lowland river, rather slow-running. North of the Liffey most of the county is rich land, based on a limestone glacial deposit. This extends southwards until the land rises into the Dublin Mountains which are of intruded granite rock and covered by poor pasture and bog. Hedges are the usual means of dividing fields except on the mountain pastures where there are stone walls. The fields are small as a rule in the rich pasture land and birds are plentiful. Except on the higher ground there is abundant parkland.

The forests are confined to the high ground to the south of the county and are mainly Sitka Spruce and Contorta Pine. An interesting one is that on the former Massey estate (on road L 94, south of Ballyboden O12) where there are stands of a variety of broad-leaved trees including Spanish Chestnut, Oak and Beech and a fine row of Monkeypuzzle in addition to the common conifers.

Two canals run across Dublin. Both carry lime-rich water and have a very rich flora and fauna. The Grand is still in active use by boats and is therefore cleared of weeds annually. The Royal has long been abandoned and has a rich growth of weed and comparison of the two makes an interesting study. In the south of the county the River Dodder O12 starts its life as a very poor mountain stream and flows southwards to join the Liffey near its mouth. It becomes enriched when it meets the limestone gravels and its lower reaches are rich and sluggish, eventually rather heavily polluted. All of the north county streams are rich and have runs of Sea Trout.

There are no natural lakes in the county and the only substantial areas of fresh water are reservoirs. Boherna-

Lowland Stream. The River Liffey downstream of Lucan. The water flows slowly and carries a heavy burden of silt; the bed of the river is muddy.

breena (south of Tallaght O02) is the largest and most attractive, set in a deep wooded valley but it is also the poorest in animal life since it was selected as a site where soft, and therefore poor, water could be collected. The ponds at Brittas O02 have rich water and in winter a number of Whooper Swan and various diving ducks gather. The ponds in Phoenix Park, especially that in the Zoo have breeding water birds including Dabchick and Coot. In the north the Bog of the Ring Reservoir, near the Naul O16 has much in common with a rich natural lake.

In spite of being one of the smaller counties Dublin has one of the largest floras in Ireland and attracts a wide variety of birds. One of the reasons for this is its long and very varied coast. There is a great expanse of sandy or shingle beach, a number of points where there are low cliffs and rocky promontories with good rock pools and some steep cliffs where seabirds breed in large numbers. There are also two excellent muddy estuaries and two sheltered lagoons. Going southwards there is interesting cliff scenery between Skerries O26 and Loughshinny where the rocks are strongly folded. The estuaries at Rush O25 and Malahide O24 attract many wading birds and duck in winter with occasional White-fronted Goose at Rush and Brent Goose at Malahide. Lambay O35, Ireland's Eye O24 and Howth O23 all have good bird cliffs. The birds on the islands are more easy to approach, the mainland ones on Howth generally build their nests out of reach. The common species are Herring Gull, Great Black-back, Kittiwake, Razorbill and Guillemot with a few Black Guillemot, Lesser Black-back and Fulmar.

The most exciting place for naturalists in Dublin is the North Bull Island (Dollymount O23) in Dublin Bay. It is a recently developed sand bank, less than two hundred years old. A walk across it from south-east to north-west traverses a variety of conditions. On the exposed south-eastern side there is a broad sandy beach; behind it lie sand dunes and then firm pasture, rich in lime from sea shells. In parts there is low land behind this with fresh-water marsh and alder bushes. Then there is an expanse of salt marsh yielding to mud flats and a sheltered lagoon. From April to September there are rather few birds – Skylark and Meadow Pipit are conspicuous and Shelduck breed – but a great variety of flowering plants. From September to April birds are dominant. They are mainly great flocks of duck and waders which breed in northern countries. Many of the species are numbered in thousands: Wigeon, Curlew.

Bar-tailed Godwit, Redshank, Knot, Oystercatcher, Golden Plover and Dunlin are some of the most numerous. There are many other duck such as Mallard, Teal, Pintail, Shoveler and Shelduck. A flock of Brent Goose can usually be seen at the northern end of the island. Besides these there are flocks of familiar species such as Herring Gull and Starling and many scarce kinds, especially in spring and autumn.

Within Dublin Bay there is much sandy or slightly muddy beach where marine worms and shellfish such as Cockle can be found. There are rock outcrops and rock pools at many points but they have incomplete faunas nowadays on account of the pollution of the water. The same situation is found further south around the rocks of Killiney O22 beach. There are more rocks and rock pools with some breeding birds to the south of Dalkey O22 and on Dalkey Island but the Howth and Ireland's Eye ones are more interesting.

Wicklow

Most of the county of Wicklow is hilly ground. The Wicklow Mountains rise to 3,039 feet at Lugnaquilla T09 and level ground is virtually limited to a narrow coastal strip. The main mass of the mountains is granite which forms a very poor soil and the higher ground is covered with blanket bog. The work of the glaciers accounts for much of the scenery, particularly the straight, deep valleys with many waterfalls and also the mountain lakes. Towards the west of the county the hills are coated with lime-rich glacial gravel and these regions are fertile in contrast to the rather barren mountains.

There is abundant parkland and the Powerscourt demesne between Djouce Mountain and Enniskerry O11 is one of the best, with the added advantage of being open to the public. It has a good arboretum and a deerpark where Red and Japanese Sika Deer may be seen. There are fine Oak trees and forestry plantations near the Waterfall which is flanked by steep cliffs with ungrazed natural vegetation. Another estate worth special attention is Avondale, just south of Rathdrum T18, once the home of Parnell, which has been State property since 1904. In the few years after it was taken over it was laid out as an experimental forest and one-acre plots of a great variety of trees were planted. These trees are now well grown and besides them there is a pinetum and a great area of woodland. The Glen of the Downs O21 has a large forest of broadleaved trees. Very little of it is true native woodland but it has many of the characteristics of a natural forest of the kind that formerly covered much of the country. There are remnants of native Oak forest at Glendalough T19, in the nearby Vale of Clara and round about Glenealy T29. Wicklow is the most densely forested county and has twenty-three State forests in all. The largest are Glenmalure T09 and Glendalough. Red Deer are widely spread in the mountains, Sika Deer and Fallow Deer are found in places.

Most of the rivers of Wicklow begin as poor mountain streams and some of them, like the Avoca T29 and its tributaries remain in that state throughout. The Avoca is unusual in being heavily polluted by toxic chemicals from old mine tips near its mouth and has no Salmon. Other rivers, like the Liffey O01 and the Slaney (Glen of Imail S99) become enriched as they pass through the glacial gravels of the lower land. The natural mountain lakes are all poor and have very little bird life. The Common Sandpiper may be seen on their shores in summer. Some of the lakes, including Glendalough and Lough Dan O10 have stocks of Char.

The Poulaphouca Reservoir N90, apart from its large size, has quite a different character. Its water is relatively rich and much of the shoreline is composed of glacial gravel rather than the bare rock and peat found around the others. It was formerly an excellent Brown Trout lake but the introduction of Perch and subsequently Pike upset the trout fishing. The breeding birds are rather limited on account of the irregular changes in the water level. These often swamp the nests of shore birds but Mallard and Teal with some Lapwing, Curlew, Snipe and Common Sandpiper are found in the breeding season. In winter many duck, especially Wigeon, come in and large flocks of Lapwing and Golden Plover gather. The Reservoir supports one of the few remaining Irish flocks of Greylag Goose and both Whooper and Bewick's Swans come regularly. The best part of the reservoir for bird-watching is the northern end. At Arklow T27 there is a small lake behind the sand dunes and this has been declared a bird sanctuary. It is a relatively shallow and very rich lake and in winter attracts Pochard and Whooper Swan. Coot, Moorhen, Dabchick and Mute Swan are present throughout the year and Kingfisher may quite often be seen.

Just south of Bray O21 where even the seashore presents the appearance of a built-up area is the rocky promontory of Bray Head. It has a large colony of breeding Herring Gull, some Fulmar, a pair of Raven and a rather unusual colony of Black Guillemot. They nest in drainage holes in the retaining wall underneath the railway line. Wicklow Head T39 had pleasant scenery and Raven but is otherwise less interesting to bird-watchers than is Bray. Between Bray and Wicklow Head the beach is sand or shingle and a number of rare seashore plants can be found. Behind the railway line from Kilcoole to Newcastle O30 and to north and south of these points there is lowlying ground drained by tidal channels. Wading birds, duck and sometimes White-fronted Goose are found there in winter and Blackheaded Gull breed in the marshes. This stretch of coast is most interesting in spring and autumn when many migrating birds visit it.

Wexford

Wexford is mostly low-lying and rather flat country, based on shaley rocks which outcrop in places on the higher ground and on the coast. A very large proportion of the area of the county is rich pasture. There is much parkland and this is best seen at Johnstown Castle, on the Rosslare road from Wexford T01, which is owned by the Agricultural Institute and is open as a park. It has a large artificial lake and a Nature Trail has been laid out. The only substantial area of high ground, yielding poor pasture and heathery slopes, is the Blackstairs Mountains S84 which are an extension of the granite of the Wicklow Mountains, reaching their highest point in Mount Leinster at 2,610 feet S85. A considerable area of their slopes has been afforested. In general elsewhere in the country the forests are planted at the tops of low hills such as Forth Mountain S90 and Camolin Forest T05. The Kennedy Memorial Forest Park and Arboretum, south-east of Dunganstown S72, was opened in 1968. It has two main parts: the arboretum which it is hoped will contain a collection of some 6,000 species of trees and shrubs and the forest garden which will contain plots of

Fallow Deer. The most widely distributed species of deer in the country. It was introduced artificially, probably by the Anglo-normans.

about 250 species of trees growing under forest conditions. There is a small, rich lake in the arboretum. Curracloe Forest T02 is one of the few areas where planting has taken place on sand at the coast. It contains a variety of trees of which Monterey Pine and Corsican Pine, planted in the early 1930's have been the most successful.

There are no natural lakes of any size in the county. The River Slaney drains a large proportion of the county and smaller rivers run to the east and south coasts. They are practically all rich lowland streams for most of their lengths. The Slaney has good stocks of Salmon and its estuary is fished successfully for Eel. The tidal portion of the Slaney, from Oilgate S93 to Wexford Harbour has extensive reed swamps by its banks and in places, especially just upstream of Wexford town, the tide leaves large mudflats bare. In the south-east there are many 'marl holes' which form small and very rich lakelets.

The coast is the most interesting feature of Wexford. On the east there are many miles of strand, backed by low cliffs of glacial gravels but the south-east and south portions are really remarkable. They are very unstable regions where the sea and the land are continually changing places. At present the great bay of Wexford Harbour is silting up and the town of Wexford is of ever-decreasing importance as a seaport. One of the new islands formed by the silting has been colonised by terns and is now an important bird sanctuary. On the south coast there are large muddy bays, surrounded by slobland at Bannow Bay S80, Killag S90 and Tomhaggard T00. All of these attract many shore birds in winter.

Lady's Island Lake T00 is probably unique in Ireland in its way of changing from a sea inlet to a freshwater lake every few years. Its outlet to the sea gets blocked by the accumulation of beach material and as drainage water flows in from the surrounding land the salt concentration is reduced. When the outlet has been open for some months the water in the lake has almost as high a salt concentration as the sea outside and Shore Crab, Flounder, Bass and Grey Mullet are the dominant inhabitants. Soon after the gap is closed the crabs die and gradually the sea fish disappear. Eel and Stickleback, freshwater fish which can tolerate salt conditions, are able to survive the whole cycle. As long as the breach is closed the water level rises within and eventually the

County Council uses a buldozer to make a new opening and release the water to prevent the surrounding land from flooding. Many water birds live on the lake in winter and summer and hundreds of Mute Swan come to moult in autumn. The lake is also a good place for migrating water birds in spring and autumn. Cotton Weed is abundant on the sea shore to the south of the lake and is not found anywhere else in the country.

The most famous region of the county is the reclaimed land on the north and south sides of Wexford Harbour called the North and South Slobs. They were formerly tidal flats but in the middle of the nineteenth Century sea walls were built which confined the water to a large central channel in each and left dry and fertile land, on either side. In dry weather the channels are able to drain into the sea at low tide. In rainy periods water accumulates too quickly for this and electric pumps are used to keep the level down. Apart from organized shoots the birds on the Slobs are unusually free from disturbance and in winter they gather in enormous numbers. A recent midwinter count gave 6,000 wild geese, 7,000 duck and 60,000 wading birds of which a third were Golden Plover. The geese are practically all White-fronts from Greenland and they make up more than half the world population of the race. The Slobs together constitute one of the finest wildfowl grounds in Europe. 450 acres of the North Slob were purchased as a reserve in 1969 and a public access with a viewing tower were built in 1970.

The rather low level of the Wexford mainland does not provide a particularly good ground for breeding cliff birds but the Saltee Islands X99 have one of the best colonies in the land. Great Saltee is the more easily accessible and provides large numbers of Herring Gull,

Kittiwake, Guillemot, Razorbill and Puffin with Great and Lesser Black-back, Shag, Shearwater and Fulmar. In autumn and spring great numbers of migrating land birds visit these islands and Great Saltee was manned by bird-watchers for many years. They discovered that, apart from the movements of many common species, a number of birds which had been considered to be rare visitors to Ireland in fact passed regularly. The Pied Flycatcher and the Redstart are typical examples. Grey Seal rest on the rocks just off the Great Saltee and sometimes breed there.

Waterford

A large proportion of the land of Waterford lies above two hundred feet and the county in general has a hilly character. There are rich green fields on the lower levels and over many of the gentle, rounded hills. The Comeraghs S21 and Knockmealdowns S00 rise to over 2,000 feet. These mountains are of sedimentary rock, sandstones, shales and slates in contrast to the igneous Wicklow range. Fallow Deer are found on both ranges. Generally speaking the Comeraghs are the more interesting of the two, having mountain lakes and cliffs in addition to heathery slopes. There are extensive forestry plantations south of Clonmel S12, along the south side of the Suir Valley S22, around Portlaw S41 and on the Drum Hills X19 in the south of the county. The steep banks of the lower reaches of the Blackwater, especially at Villierstown X19 are richly forested. Much of this is long established and dense broad-leaved woodland. The Red Squirrel is a common inhabitant. Fallow Deer are kept at Ballinatry Estate, north of Youghal X07.

Around the highest point of the Comeraghs, 2,597 feet, there are mountain lakes with poor water one of which, Coomshingaun, has a stock of Char. Ballin Lough is a small, rich lake to the north of Kill S40 and has a good winter wildfowl population. Apart from these and a small rich lake to the east of Woodstown S60 there is little in the way of still water. The River Suir, which forms the county boundary with Tipperary, is a large and unusually straight rich lowland river with a fertile flood plain. The freshwater part of the Blackwater is similar to the Suir and both rivers have long tidal portions with extensive reed beds and small islands and creeks.

A large proportion of the sea coast is rocky with small bays and coves with sandy or shingle beaches. In the month of May there is a magnificent display of seashore flowers along the coast road, especially at Bunmahon X49 where Sea Pink blooms in profusion with contrasting yellow Kidney Vetch and white Sea Campion. The Waterford coast is the most easterly part of the range of the Chough which is quite a common cliff bird around Annestown S49 and elsewhere. At Dunmore East S60 there is a cliff colony of Kittiwake and west of Helvick Head S38 there are good bird cliffs with Herring Gull, Kittiwake, Shag, Razorbill and Guillemot among others. In winter the most interesting bird haunts are the Back Strand at Tramore S50 and Dungarvan Harbour S21 where there are mud flats and salt marsh sheltered by a sand bar.

Dunmore East in winter is one of the most active fishing ports on the coast. Its importance is entirely due to the annual gathering of Herring off the Waterford coast. For most of the year the fish are spread out over a large area of sea so that fishing for them is not an economic

proposition. Towards the end of the year they form dense shoals and lay their eggs, scattering again soon afterwards. The shoaling and hence the fishing season ends in February.

Cork

Cork is the largest county of Ireland and the city of Cork is the third in size. It offers a good range of urban conditions from barren docks and industrial areas to pleasant suburbs and parkland on the outskirts. A particularly interesting area is The Lough, to the south of University College, where the small lake has a good population of water fowl. The River Lee W57 is fairly heavily polluted but has a good run of Salmon and in the city itself Grey Mullet can often be seen in summer, swimming slowly near the surface. Within the city area there are extensivie mudflats by the banks of the Lee where wading birds and gulls gather in large numbers in winter.

Throughout the county rich pasture and parkland is found mainly on the low ground of the valleys of the large rivers and to some extent in the low-lying coastal regions. Poor hill pasture is the dominant condition of land. Blarney W67 has a particularly good area of parkland and broad-leaved wood in the Castle demesne. Forestry plantations are many and Cork has the greatest area of forest in the country. Most of the forests are on the higher ground, following the main mountain ranges.

St. Patrick's Cabbage. One of the most striking of the Hiberno-Lusitanian plants.

Inchigeelagh Forest W26 which runs around the lakes of the upper reaches of the Lee includes a forest park at Gougane Barra W06 with fine viewing roads and a nature trail. At Glengariff V95 there is a good deal of old Oak forest and this has been carefully preserved in the course of modern planting. A nature trail has been laid out. The planted wood includes, besides Sitka Spruce and Contorta Pine, Silver Fir, Hemlock Spruce, Beech, Eucalyptus and Poplars. The coastal parts of west Cork are unusual in Ireland in having a climate virtually free from frost and many southern plants thrive in the open.

Native wild plants of particular interest are the Great Butterwort, Irish Spurge and St Patrick's Cabbage (a saxifrage, also known as London Pride). The Butterwort is an insectivorous plant which thrives in bog conditions, Irish Spurge grows in open pasture and stands out clearly in May when its leaves are yellowish in contrast with the darker green of the grass. St Patrick's Cabbage is found in plenty on damp cliffs and rocky surfaces where the soil is poor. The three are abundant in west Cork and in Kerry and are scarce elsewhere in the country. They are some of the most striking members of a group of plants known as 'Hiberno-Lusitanian' which have their main centres of distribution here and in Spain and Portugal.

Peaty soil conditions are prevalent in Cork west of a line from Mallow W59 to Rosscarbery W23 and on the higher parts of Nagle's Mountains W69. An unusual wetland area is the Gearagh, west of Macroom W16. The River Lee here breaks up into a number of clear streams and divides the land into a network of small wooded islands where grazing animals are unable to go. It is rich in plants and insect life. The Gearagh was formely quite extensive but its area has been greatly reduced by the flooding of the valley to form the Lee Reservoir.

The drainage of Cork follows a remarkably constant pattern. The three great rivers Blackwater W39, Lee and Bandon W45 all rise in the west as poor mountain streams and flow eastwards parallel to the main axes of the mountain ranges and then turn abruptly southwards to reach the sea by long winding estuaries running south or south-west. Their lower reaches are rich and many parts of the valleys are beautifully wooded on both sides. The Blackwater is the only Irish river with Dace and one of the very few with true Roach. Both were introduced artificially in the nineteenth century. The Dace live in gravelly stretches of water similar to those required as nursery areas by Salmon and breed much faster. Since their introduction they have caused a considerable reduction in the salmon stocks.

Near the headwaters of the Lee is Gougane Barra Lake W06 which has rather poor water but is beautifully situated in forest hills. Some way downstream the river widens again into Lough Allua W26 and a large proportion of its lower reaches have been impounded by two dams to form extensive reservoirs. These lakes form the greatest area of freshwater in the county but are not very rich in wild life. Small poor lakes are scattered through the south-west of the county and there is a group of mountain lakes in the Caha mountains to the east of Glengariff.

The coast of Cork is long and broken up by many inlets and headlands large and small. There are few extensive beaches – the largest is in Ballycotton Bay W26 – but numerous rocky coves and sheltered bays. Behind the shore at Ballycotton there is a good area of marsh and reed swamp with a small rich lake. Duck and waders breed here and some, like the Black-tailed Godwit, which are normally winter visitors, stay throughout the summer. From autumn to spring this is a very good region for water birds and some American species are recorded fairly regularly.

Seabird cliffs are few and rather inaccessible. The best are on the Bull and Cow Rocks V43 where there are Gannet and the only Storm Petrel in the county besides the more common coastal species. Any of the headlands are likely to be good points for watching migrating birds and to see ocean species but Cape Clear has become established as one of the most interesting of its kind. A bird observatory has been manned there for some years and a remarkable list of species has been recorded, most of them during the spring and autumn migrations. As in the case of Saltee many birds, considered to be extremely rare on the mainland, have been shown to be regular visitors. The ocean birds include Albatross, Great Shearwater and Sooty Shearwater. These are exceptional amongst birds seen in Europe because they breed in the southern hemisphere and migrate northwards in winter (our summer). The majority of birds in Europe migrate south. Other aspects of the natural history of Cape Clear are being studied and a book on the island is to be published.

The most interesting of the coves of Cork is Lough Hyne W02 which is a sea lough with conditions unique in Ireland. In the first place there is extremely little fresh water flowing in and secondly the outlet is narrow and blocked by a sill of rock so that the water level never falls below half tide mark. In effect it is an enormous rock pool and has a very rich and varied fauna. Fishes such as Pipefish and Sucker can be found easily by turning over stones. Many other creatures like Starfish and

Sea Urchin which are normally difficult to approach without diving gear can be seen. Wading will reveal many forms of life but a boat is helpful since the shore in most of the parts accessible by road is very steep. Grey Seal breed on islands in Roaringwater Bay V93.

Kerry

Kerry offers much of the finest scenery in Ireland and probably has the greatest variety of communities. Rich land is the scarcest type and is found round about Tralee Q81 and Castleisland R00, in the lower part of the valley of the Laune V89, round about Kenmare V79 and on parts of the coast. The county north of a line from Killorglin V78 to Rathmore W19 consists mostly of low hills with poor soil and peat on the higher ground. The southern part and the Dingle peninsula is much more mountainous, rising to over 3,000 feet in the Reeks V88 and on Brandon Q41. Most of the soil is peaty. The county has a peculiar flora and fauna with the Lusitanian plants making a particularly fine show. As in west Cork Great Butterwort, St Patrick's Cabbage and Irish Spurge are plentiful. The Kerry Slug, a splendid spotted species, may be seen crawling over damp rocks in many parts of the county (its range also extends to west Cork). Elsewhere it is found only in Portugal and the Pyrenees.

The Killarney V99 region is well forested and contains some of the most extensive native Oak woods in the country. The most interesting tree there is the Arbutus which is typically a Mediterranean plant and is otherwise extremely rare outside Kerry. Red Deer are plentiful and represent the only herd in the country containing the native stock. Sika Deer and Fallow Deer have been introduced. A large area of the district, the Bourn Vincent memorial Park, is State property and is managed so that its scenery may be preserved. It is one of the few regions where old cultivated forest still exists and this includes Sitka Spruce, Douglas Fir, Larch, Corsican Pine and Scots Pine. State planting has included all of the common conifers and also Hemlock Spruce and Eucalyptus. The forests on the shores of Kenmare River, west of Templenoe W86 have Monterey Pine, Silver Fir, Beech and Oak besides the common conifers. Rhododendron grows luxuriantly but it is an introduced species and, unless kept in check, is liable to do severe damage to the natural vegetation. Goats are another source of harm. While the Killarney area contains the most magnificent examples of the Kerry woodlands it suffers from its general popularity as a tourist region. A smaller centre is found in the vicinity of Cloonee V66 on the south side of Kenmare River where the flora is much the same and observers are more likely to be left in peace. As in Killarney the lake islands give the best examples of the flora, untouched by grazing animals.

Blanket bog is widely distributed, occuring on the high ground around Cahirciveen V47, Lough Cara V79, Rathmore W19, east of Mount Brandon, north of Inch V69 and over large areas of the Glanruddery Q91 and Mullaghareirk R12 Mountains. Poorly drained and marshy ground is the rule in Kerry rather than the exception. There are extensive reed swamps by the Cashen River Q38.

The rivers of Kerry are all comparatively short and poor. The species of fish, such as Perch, Pike, Rudd and Bream which require rich water are virtually absent from the county and Trout and Salmon thrive. The Brown Trout are mostly small and Sea Trout are very

Sea Pink. On uninhabited islands off Kerry this forms a thick turf with many hummocks.

common. In Lough Currane V56 they are often exceptionally large by Irish standards, many weighing three to four pounds. The river water is usually bright and clear and the Dipper is a common bird.

Lakes are numerous and range in size from Loughs Leane V98 and Currane to small mountain tarns. They are poor and have relatively little bird life. Teal and Mallard breed by many of the larger ones and the Merganser is found in Lough Leane. Common Tern nest on Lough Currane. There are stocks of Char in the Killarney lakes and in Lough Currane and probably elsewhere. A form of Shad, called the Killarney Shad, is occasionally caught there and appears to be a completely freshwater form – normally Shad breed in fresh or brackish water and migrate to sea.

The coast of Kerry is greatly extended by the long, narrow bays of Kenmare River and Dingle Bay. These are both 'drowned' river valleys, shaped by rivers in the past when the level of the land was higher. High or low cliffs predominate but most other forms of coast may be found on the mainland. The Chough is a common bird in the cliff regions. There are fine sandy beaches with sand dunes in Ballinskelligs Bay V46, at the Inch, at Castlegregory Q61, Banna Strand Q72 and Ballybunnion Q64. Of these the Inch is especially interesting as the only part of Ireland where toads are found. The species is the Natterjack but it is nocturnal and therefore seldom seen. There is extensive salt marsh in Castlemaine Harbour Q70 and the River Cashen has a good muddy estuary. Tralee Bay and Barrow Harbour Q71 also offer salt marsh and mud flats with beds of Zostera grass which attracts many duck and wild geese. These bays all have good flocks of wintering waterfowl, especially Brent Goose and Wigeon. Tralee Bay and Castlemaine Harbour together form the most important Brent Goose haunt in the country. Dingle Bay has comparatively shallow water at its eastern end and a large flock of Common Scoter usually spends the winter there. The inner part of the bay, sheltered by sandbanks, is an important centre for Mussel fishing and Tralee Bay has some of the best Oyster beds.

Seabirds nest on the cliffs along the mainland but not in large numbers. Some of the offshore islands, however, have enormous colonies. The Little Skellig V26, a bird sanctuary, has a population of Gannet estimated to be 10,000 pairs. The island is difficult to land on due to the usual heavy swell but even to sail close to it is an experience. The Great Skellig close by has several thousand pairs of Storm Petrel, many of which nest between the stones of the walls of the 'beehive' cells of the old monastery. Puffin Island V36 has a very large colony of Shearwater and the Tearaght V19 offers thousands of Puffin which are remarkably easy to approach. Inishvickillane V29 is also a good bird island with many Storm Petrel and the added advantage of being a more comfortable place to stay. All of the bird islands have large or small populations of the more common cliff birds in addition to their specialties. A number of the islands, including Inishvickillane and Inishtooskert Q20 have an unusual greensward consisting mostly of Sea Pink. In places this develops its own soil, a material similar to peat, which was used by the islanders as fuel. Where it is untouched it forms hummocks, some of them two or three feet in height. Grey Seal are common around the islands.

Just inland of Ballyheige Bay Q27 is Lough Akeragh which has become one of the most celebrated winter bird haunts in the county. It is a small, shallow and rich lake and attracts various species of duck, especially the Gadwall which is otherwise rather rare in Ireland. Besides these many migrating waterfowl stop there and some American species are annual visitors. Brandon Bay has a population of Terns and Common Gull and Skuas may be seen there more often than in most parts of Ireland.

Limerick

The city of Limerick is dominated by the River Shannon. In spite of the size of the river there is a certain amount of pollution but Salmon are still able to pass through it and there is an important fishery for them at Thomond Weir, just upstream of the city. An interesting fish which quite frequently reaches Limerick is the Smelt, a small silvery species which lives in salt or brackish water but moves far up the estuaries to spawn in March or April. The Shannon estuary is its only known habitat in Ireland. Gulls are plentiful in the city, especially on the rubbish heaps and at points where sewage enters the rivers.

The typical land of the county is rich with a great many well wooded estates and numerous hedges. Poor pasture is comparatively scarce but may be found on the higher ground, especially the Galtee R82 and Ballyhoura Mountains R61. Lusitanian plants extend into the county: Irish Spurge is widespread to the south and west and St Patrick's Cabbage grows on the Galty Mountains where there are also many species of alpine plants. At Askeaton R35 there is some bare limestone, similar to that found in Clare but with a poorer flora. Afforestation has not taken place to any great degree and amounts to about 11,000 acres, most of it on the high land, as on the Slievefelim Mountains R75. There is some interesting woodland just east of Foynes L25. Blanket bog occurs mostly in the west of the county, on the Mullaghareirk Mountains R12, on the hills west of Newcastle West R23 and to the north-east at Castleconnell R66.

The rivers of Limerick are rich lowland ones over most of their lengths. The main ones are the Feale R12, the Maigue R44, the Deel R34 and the Mulkear R65. The Flounder, a flat fish normally associated with the sea and estuaries travels well into the fresh water of the Maigue but moves back to salt water to breed. It is found in some other rivers but usually has its path blocked by a waterfall or weir before it can go far. The lakes of Limerick are small and rich. The best known is

Lough Gur R64 which, in addition to an interesting flora, is noted for the large numbers of bones of the extinct Great Irish Deer which have been found in the muds and marshes around it.

The sea shore is mostly muddy estuary with long, winding inlets where subsidiary rivers join it. In winter various wading birds and duck may be seen there and White-fronted Goose are found near Mungret. Coastal diving birds like Great Crested Grebe and Redthroated Diver are fairly common. Terns are plentiful in summer and breed on low-lying islands. An interesting plant is the Triangular Club-rush which is abundant on both banks of the Shannon estuary from Limerick for some miles downstream but unknown elsewhere in the country. From Limerick to Foynes there are great stretches of mud flat, wet meadows and ditches very difficult to reach without a boat. They should be rich in bird and plant life but have not been thoroughly explored.

Clare

Clare is one of the most interesting counties. It contains examples of all of the main communities with some of the most extreme conditions in the land added for good measure. Much of the lower ground is pasture bordering between rich and poor with a great deal of marshy land. To the east the Slieve Aughty M06 mountains have very poor peaty soil. There is blanket bog on the higher ground to the west, most of it on a line from Ennis R37 to Kilkee Q68 and in two outlying places, Slieve Elva M01 and south of Lisdoonvarna R21. The Slieve Elva bog is bordered on three sides by the opposite community, bare limestone.

Small Tortoiseshell Butterfly. One of the first butterflies to appear in spring. Adults which emerge in autumn spend the winter in hibernation and can take advantage of early flowers.

There is parkland on a small scale around Bunratty Castle R46 and more extensively in the Dromoland Castle demesne (north of Newmarket-on-Fergus R46). At Dromore, between Ruan and Crusheen R38 there is fine woodland with rich lakes and the Pine Marten is well established. Cratloe Wood R46 contains some native forest. Kilrush Forest R05 is a long established plantation, first laid out in 1814. Nearly one hundred years later it was taken over by Forestry Division and extended. It has many fine old trees from the earlier plantings, including Ash, Oak, Beech, Sycamore, Elm and Silver Fir. In the east of the county there are extensive plantations on the hills overlooking Lough Derg as at Tuamgraney R68. Towards the coast trees seldom thrive but there is extensive Hazel scrub and many small Hazel woods on the limestone in the north and west of the county. Some of these woods have Pine Marten.

The Burren region of Clare, that is the north-east corner, is famous for its great area of limestone rock. There are isolated fields and Hazel woods but otherwise the prevailing colour is grey, relieved by bright little patches of grass and wild flowers. These conditions are found at their best around Black Head M11 and Ballyvaughan M12. Dryas, Blue Gentian and Hypnoid Saxifrage are abundant, the Dryas being a conspicuous roadside flower in May. Such flowers are common on the Alps and other high montains but can thrive down to sea level in Clare. Maidenhair fern is not so easy to find and should not be picked as too much collecting in the past has reduced the stock. A little later in the year the Dark Red Helleborine Orchid flowers in the crevices.

The insects of the Burren are also extremely interesting. A butterfly, the Pearl Bordered Fritillary and a moth, the Burren Green are quite common there and not found anywhere else in the country. Another common Burren moth, the Transparent Burnet, is also rare outside the region. The Burren Green, known from continental Europe, was not found until 1949 but has since proved to be plentiful in Clare. Butterflies and moths are the most popular insects for study and there can be no doubt that many of the less known insect groups are represented by rarities in the Burren.

Lough Derg is a rich lake with well-wooded shores and many islands, especially in the County Clare portion. The most interesting fish there is the Pollan, like the Char a survivor from a period when the climate was colder. It feeds on planktonic animals, amongst them a Mysid which is also a relict species and confined to a few lakes in the country. There are extensive beds of reeds and rushes and many species of waterfowl breed. Great Crested Grebe and Dabchick, Moorhen and Coot, Mallard, Teal, Tufted Duck and Merganser, Blackheaded Gull and Common Tern are all plentiful in summer and many more duck come in winter. Downstream of Lough Derg the level of the Shannon is controlled at Parteen weir (north of Montpelier R66) and there and at the generating station at Ardnacrusha (Power Station R56) there are fish passes to allow Salmon and Eel to migrate. At Killaloe R77 Eel on their way to breed are caught by the ton in autumn in nets hung just downstream of the bridge.

The other lakes of the county range from large and small poor ones such as Graney R59 and Doo R17 to extremely rich types like Inchiquin R28 and Bunny R39. The rich ones in general are found on the low ground and are usually well provided with reed beds and have considerable areas of fenland around them. Some lakes, like Inchiquin, are relatively shallow and support a dense growth of weeds on their beds. Others, like Lough George R39, plunge to more than 50 feet and, in spite of their very rich water and shorelines are poor in the quantity of living creatures. Besides the many permanent lakes there are numerous turloughs in the central part of the county, on a line from Gort M40 to Ennis R37 but these are better developed in Galway.

In the east of the county poor mountain streams flow down into Lough Derg. The central part drains into the River Fergus R29 and 37. It is a very rich lowland river through most of its length and joins the Shannon by a very large muddy estuary with many lowlying islands. Smelt are found in the estuary. In the west the rivers are relatively short and flow direct to the Atlantic. The Cullenagh R18 (or Inagh) River has a spectacular waterfall at Ennistymon. These falls prevented the migration of salmon upstream until a fish pass was built in the 1960s. The limestone region in the north-west is almost devoid of open water since the rock is highly soluble and most of the drainage is underground. There are numerous caves in the district. One of the few rivers, the Caher (Formayle M01) is unusual in flowing over bare rock with very little deposition of silt or gravel.

The south coast of Clare is, like the coast of Limerick, lowlying with extensive salt marsh and mud flats. The west and north coasts are mainly rocky with much cliff scenery, rising to the magnificent heights of the Cliffs of Moher R09. These cliffs support a large colony of the more common cliff-nesting seabirds, which are easy to see but impossible to approach. Chough are common along most of the Atlantic coast. On Loop Head there is a large area of Sea Pink sward and a good deal of ground covered by Sea Plantain.

Galway

Galway is sharply divided into two contrasting areas. East and south of Lough Corrib the land is flat or gently rolling and based on limestone. To the west it is either flat or mountainous and in both cases underlain by acid rock. The city of Galway includes a good range of conditions from dockland to parks but water is its main feature. The River Corrib, joining the sea, breaks up into a number of streams and Galway is in effect built on several islands. The watercourses have mostly been contained by walls and several canals and millstreams have been built over the years but a great variety of natural aquatic habitats remain. The water in all parts is very rich and there is a dense growth of weeds in most parts. The most famous feature of Galway's waterways is the Salmon Weir Bridge. From spring to autumn large numbers of Salmon can be seen just upstream of the bridge when the water in the river is too low to induce them to swim up the fish pass in the barrage. In May and June Sea Lamprey may be seen in the same place and Black-headed Gull are plentiful, especially in early summer when the elver migration is in progress. There is good parkland close to the city at Merlin Park hospital and one of the finest Beech woods in Ireland at Barna, west of the city.

In east and south Galway the land is relatively rich but the soil, as in Clare, is rather shallow in many parts. There is peaty soil and blanket bog to the south on the Slieve Aughty Mountains M60 and the eastern part of the county reaches into the raised bog region in the River Suck valley from Ballygar M75 nearly to Ballinasloe M83. An area of this bog based on Ahascragh M73 and including a portion of untouched bog margin has been acquired by An Taisce to be preserved as an example of the habitat.

West Galway is completely different, with the exception of a narrow strip east of the main road from Galway to Oughterard M14 where the limestone appears. The soil is poor, peaty and very badly drained and the scenery is dominated by high, barren mountains, the Twelve Pins L75 and Maumturk L85 in particular. A number of interesting plants are found in the area. One of the most striking is St Dabeoc's Heath, another of the Hiberno-lusitanian plants, which is confined to Galway and Mayo and not found again closer than SW France. It is the most widely distributed of a remarkable group of heathers found in Connemara. Mackey's Heath is found only in the Roundstone Region L74: round about Craigga-more Lough 4 miles W of N of Roundstone and at Carna, 6½ miles to the SE. Mediterranean Heath is found over a wider range to the north of Roundstone. Fuchsia, an introduced plant, thrives in these parts.

The bare limestone, seen at its best in Clare, outcrops in a number of places, around the coast near Kinvarra M31 and further inland at Ross Lake M23 which also offers a good deal of fenland. The southern part has very much the same character as the burren limestone but at Ross Lake some of the more notable plants are absent. Parts of Galway have thick deposits of lime-rich glacial gravels. There are several small ridges of this in Galway Bay, a good example being Gentian Hill, just west of Salthill M22. An outlying region of drumlin land is found at the northern end of Lough Corrib.

There is good parkland in the Ashford Castle grounds at Cong M15 with a fine variety of exotic conifers. In 1884 Contorta Pine, which has proved one of the most important forest trees in Ireland, was first planted there. Coole M40 also has good parkland with a rich lake and forestry plantations. Beech, Ash and Silver Fir thrive there and grow from seed. The largest forest area in the county is in the Cloosh Valley between Oughterard and the coast in Galway Bay where Sitka Spruce, Contorta Pine and Birch are planted on over 10,000 acres of deep blanket bog. There are many smaller forests both in the Slieve Aughty Mountains and by Lough Derg. Close to Gort M40 Garryland Wood is a particularly good example of native woodland. Oak and Ash are dominant with Elm, Blackthorn, Crabapple, Holly, Spindle Tree, Guelder Rose and many others. The forests at Gort, Woodford M70 and Portumna M80 have Fallow Deer herds.

The county is abundantly supplied with rivers and

lakes. East of a line roughly from Castlerea M68 to Woodford drainage goes towards the Shannon, mostly by its tributary the Suck. Marshy ground is abundant and upstream of Portumna the Shannon floods in winter to provide 'callow' lands with great flocks of waterfowl. The tributary streams north of Ballinasloe are poor, to the south they are richer and the Suck itself is a rich, rather slow-flowing river. South of Ballinasloe there is a branch of the Grand Canal. The Galway part of Lough Derg is similar to the Clare portion. In the south-west of the county most of the drainage is by short, rich rivers to Galway Bay with the exception of Lough Cutra which runs out to the Fergus. The best known wetland area is Rahasane Turlough, two miles west of Craughwell M52. This is one of the most important wildfowl resorts in Ireland and holds thousands of duck in winter with hundreds of Whooper and Bewick's Swans and some White-fronted Goose. Other wildfowl areas are the turloughs of Ross Abbey and Turloughcor, both near Headford M24 and Killower, near Tuam M45. The east Galway rivers flowing into Lough Corrib are rich and slow. Much of the ground they drain is low-lying and marshy although the water level has been lowered by drainage operations. In the west of the county lakes and rivers are poor. The dominant fish are Sea Trout and Salmon which need relatively little food in the freshwater. Brown Trout and Eel in the west are small and slow-growing. Mallard, Teal, Snipe and Common Sandpiper breed around many of the lakes but throughout the area the population of birds is very sparse.

Pipewort. A rare water plant of the west of Ireland, common in eastern parts of North America.

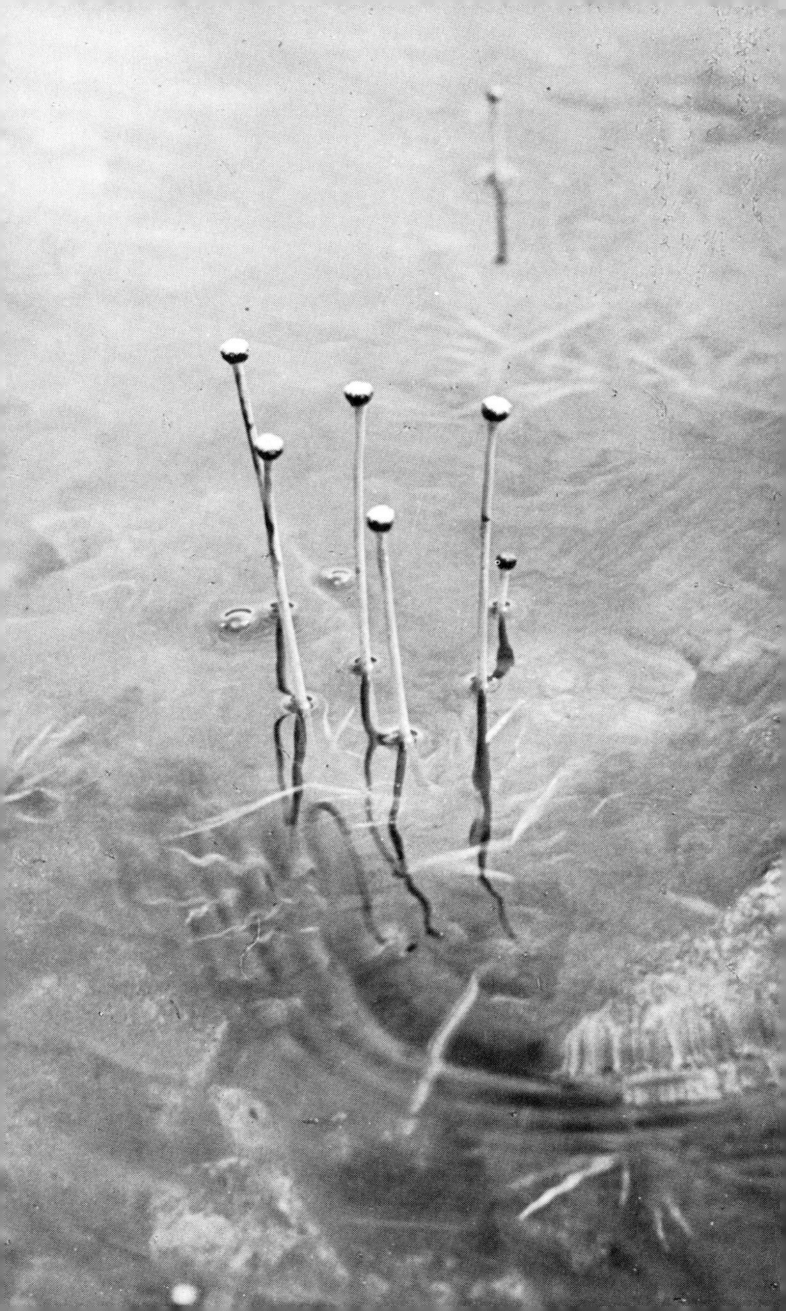

Lough Corrib is a large lake with rich water. It falls into two parts. South of Annaghdown M23 it is open and shallow, mostly less than six feet and often less than three feet in depth. The clear water allows penetration of strong light and the bottom is richly carpeted with water weed. The weed supports a dense population of invertebrates and the fish that depend on them grow fast. The northern part of the lake is much deeper with a rather narrow margin of shallow water. Its population of fish is very much less dense than in the south and, in spite of the rich water, the growth of species such as Eel is very slow. The Char is common in the northern area. The lake islands are very rich in plant and animal life. The larger ones are mostly grazed and are dominated by well-cropped grass and Gorse and Hawthorn. The smaller ones and Inchagoill M14 are free from grazing animals and there is a fine cover of natural vegetation. Scots Pine was planted on some of them in the nineteenth century. Common Gull, Tufted Duck and Merganser breed on the islands which have a good cover of shrubs. Black-headed Gull and Common Tern make their nests on the more open, low-lying ones. The variety of habitats and the sharp contrasts between the different types of islands and parts of the lake make Lough Corrib as a whole an exceptionally interesting region for study.

Galway has a very long coast line, broken into many bays with a great number of islands large and small. In the northern part of the county, especially around Ballynakill Harbour L66 and at Clifden L65 there are large sea inlets with abundant salt marsh. Most of the coast is low-lying, backed by shingle or muddy shores. Sandy beaches are small and scattered. Roundstone R74 is probably the best centre for sand with sand dunes and it also provides rocky ground with beautiful rock pools.

Between Salthill and Barna M22 is the Lough Rusher bird sanctuary which has a fair population of wintering shore birds, duck and waders.

The Aran Islands are a continuation of the Clare limestone and have a similar flora. There are bird cliffs on Inishmore. Inishbofin L55 shares with the Aran islands the attraction of having good accommodation and offers very different conditions. The ground is mostly poor with much cut-away blanket bog. The flora is interesting and a number of species rare elsewhere are easy to find. The Spotted Rock Rose is common and the Pipewort grows in several of the lakes. It is found scattered through the west of Ireland, also on some Scottish islands and in America but nowhere else in Europe. Most of the lakes are poor but a small area of blown sand at the eastern end of the island provides limey conditions of soil and there is a small rich lake with a dense growth of vegetation. There is a fine Plaintain sward at the west end of the island. The nearby Inishturk is uninhabited and has some breeding seabirds. The Grey Seal breeds on Slyne Head L54.

Mayo

Most of the land of Mayo is poor and wet. The higher ground is nearly all underlain by acid rock but there is a certain amount of outcropping limestone, mostly around Loughs Mask and Conn. Two of the main towns, Castlebar M19 and Westport M08 lie in drumlin country and the most fertile parts of the county lie on this axis. The most barren and mountainous parts are found to the west of a line from Lough Conn G10 to Lough Mask M16, both of which have acid ground on their western shores and limestone to the east. The Mayo limestones are a continuation of the Clare and Galway regions but have fewer of the outstanding plants. There is good parkland in Westport Demesne.

The largest forest estate is that on the Nephin Beg mountains F90 which occupies nearly 9,000 acres. The ground is deep blanket bog. At Glenamoy F93 Forestry Divison runs an experimental plantation where many species of trees are grown on the bog to determine the best types for planting in such regions. In the south-west of the county there are several forestry plantations in the valleys, for example at Doo Lough L86, and several regions of native Oak woods. These are found at Old Head L88, in the valley of the Erriff L96 and on the islands of Loughs Mask and Conn. In general the land is so exposed and wet that tree growth is very limited and trees are virtually absent from the coast. Rhododendron, an introduced plant, grows well in many places.

The north-western part of the county is dominated by an enormous expanse of blanket bog. This is exploited as fuel on a large scale in the Bellacorick region F92 and the possibilities of farming it are studied at Glenamoy. The Glenamoy district is also being used as a centre for the study of the ecology of peat bog in connection with the International Biological Programme. The Mayo bog is exceedingly barren with remarkably little in the way of plant or animal life. Golden Plover are believed to breed there in addition to Meadow Pipit and other typical bogland birds.

The rivers and lakes in the west of the county are, like those in west Galway, poor and have Sea Trout and Salmon as their dominant fish. At Newport L99 the Salmon Research Trust of Ireland has an experimental station set up to investigate, among other things, the reason why some Salmon return to breed after little more than a year at sea while others stay away for eighteen months or more. Carrowmore Lake F82 has a number of low-lying islands where Common Gull and Sandwich Tern breed. There are many mountain lakes in all of the hill regions and on Achill Island. The River Moy G21 is the largest of the north Mayo rivers. It receives rich water from Lough Conn and poor from its eastern tributaries. The main river flows through extensive marsh land but recent drainage operations may alter the character of this.

The large lakes Conn, Carra M17 and Mask and the Castlebar lakes are all rich ones. The first three have many islands which offer ungrazed natural vegetation and many breeding birds, much the same as in Lough Corrib. Lough Carra is a peculiar lake. Its water is exceptionally clear and rich in lime and its bottom is covered with a soft, limey deposit, white or creamy white in colour. This gives the water a beautiful pellucid green appearance. The deposit inhibits the growth of submerged plants and there is no carpet of water weed of the kind which would be expected otherwise in such clear water. There are, however, extensive beds of emergent reeds in the shallower parts. The clear water over the whitish bed makes fish stand out clearly in bright, calm weather. Brown Trout grow exceptionally quickly although the stocks of invertebrates do not seem to be unusually large. Possibly the lack of cover for the food animals makes it easier for the Trout to find them. Carra is believed to have the largest stocks of breeding Mallard in the country and these are being studied by the Agricultural Institute. The lake and the surrounding land are preserved as a wildfowl refuge.

The Mayo coast is long and offers some of the finest

cliff scenery in Ireland. Killary Harbour, with steep sides and very little foreshore forms the southernmost portion. The west coast south of Clew Bay has extensive sandy beaches. Clew Bay L88 itself is rather low-lying and marshy and at its eastern end has a large number of islands, the tips of submerged drumlins. These islands are well grazed and have rather little natural vegetation. The north coast of Mayo has a line of magnificent cliffs with great seabird colonies, especially between Porturlin and Belderg F94. Storm Petrel breed on the Stags of Broadhaven, some miles to the north. Very large numbers of Salmon swim westwards along the coast and are caught by drift nets, set across their path. Tagging showed that while most of them were local fish on their way to Mayo rivers some were going to distant places including Scotland, Wales and Sweden. Killala Bay G23,

Mediterranean Heather. The largest and most imposing of the three rare species of heather which grow in the west. This clump is on a little island on the shore of Lough Furnace, Co. Mayo.

the mouth of the River Moy has sand banks and sand hills on its western side. It is a good place for wintering wildfowl.

There are many large islands off the west coast. The first, Inishturk L67, is a good bird island in summer and has a flora similar to but richer than that of Inishbofin. Clare Island L68 is probably the most thoroughly explored piece of land in Ireland. From 1909 to 1911 a team of scientists studied its flora and fauna, 100 workers in all took part. The results were published in three volumes as *The Clare Island Survey*. 5,269 species of animals and 3,219 species of plants were recorded and folklore, geology and archaeology were also studied. The island has fine cliffs and rather inaccessible seabird colonies. Most of the ground is blanket bog or peaty soil.

Achill is the largest Irish island – or was, since it has long been joined to the mainland by a bridge. Except on the splendid cliffs the ground is damp and heathy with blanket bog over a wide area. Rhododendron has become very well established. There are several poor lakes and Pipewort is abundant around those on the east side. In summer considerable numbers of Basking Shark come into Keem Bay F50 where they are caught in nets for their valuable liver oil. The fishery is not regulated and from time to time becomes uneconomical and is abandoned for some years. The Bills Rocks, to the west of Achill, have seabird colonies including a large population of Puffin.

The Mullet F63 is not an island strictly speaking but its connection with the mainland at Belmullet F73 is so narrow that it makes little difference. In contrast to Achill it is mostly low-lying with a maximum height of 434 feet at Fower Hill F73 in the north. The low ground is overlain by blanket bog to the east and with extensive sand dunes to the west. There are many poor lakes. This is the nesting ground of the Red-necked Phalarope, one of the rarest breeding species in Ireland. It is an extremely interesting bird, among other peculiarities the female develops the brighter colours and takes the more active part in preparations for mating. The male broods the eggs. It is an Arctic bird, the Mullet colony lying far south of its normal range. A curious coincidence is that most of the very few Snowy Owl seen in Ireland have also been reported from the Mullet. This owl is another Arctic bird and may be attracted there by the same conditions that make the region suitable for the Phalaropes. The Phalarope nesting place is a bird sanctuary. To the west of the Mullet are the Inishkea Islands F52 which are important as the main wintering ground for Barnacle Goose in Ireland, a flock of more than 2,000 are regular visitors. Grey Seal breed on Inishturk, Caher Island L67, Clare Island and Achill Head. They haul out on the Inishkeas in summer but apparently do not breed there.

Sligo

Sligo offers a very wide variety of conditions in a comparatively small area. The underlying material is partly limestone and partly acid metamorphic rock, both kinds provide fine mountain scenery. A belt of drumlin land occupies much of the south of the county and provides reasonably rich pasture. There is also good land between the mountains and the coast, where there is limerich glacial gravel. The Ox Mountains G42 provide a large area of peaty uplands and there is extensive blanket bog there and between Tubbercurry G51 and Bellahy G43. The Benbulbin G64 range, Knocknarea G63 and the Keshcorran and Carrowkeel Hills to the west of Lough Arrow G71 are limestone hills. They are topped with blanket bog but their steep sides and screes are limestone so the two opposite conditions of acid bog and basic limestone may be found together. The Benbulbin range in particular is exceptionally rich in Alpine flowers which grow on the limestone slopes. They include many of the Burren plants such as Dryas and Hypnoid Saxifrage but have others like Irish Sandwort and Clustered Alpine Saxifrage which are not found elsewhere in the country. The caves of Kesh G71 have been excavated and the bones of many animals now extinct in Ireland were found, including Bear, Arctic Lemming and Reindeer.

There are large forestry plantations on poor ground on the Ox Mountains and to the north-east of Collooney G62. Lough Gill Forest G73, first planted in 1939, lies on richer ground than usual and Hemlock Spruce, Silver Firs and Cypresses grow with some broad-leaved trees in addition to all of the common conifers. Around Lough Gill lies some of the finest native forest in the country. It is mainly Oak wood with the usual underlying Holly but, as in Killarney, Arbutus is common. Slish Wood, on the south shore of the lake besides the Oak has Birch, Holly, Hazel, a little Arbutus and a very rich growth of ferns and mosses. At Mullaghmore Maritime Pine and Scots Pine have been grown very successfully on the sand dunes for over a century.

Most of the drainage of Sligo is by rather short, swift rivers which rise and reach the sea within the county. An exception is found on the Ox Mountains where the Moy rises and flows inland into Mayo where it turns north to Killala Bay. Its upper waters are poor but it becomes enriched lower down. The northwestern slopes of the Ox Mountains have a number of bog lakes which drain into the Easky River G33, with a more direct course to the sea. The other lakes and rivers are rich ones. Loughs Gill and Arrow G71 have many islands with ungrazed woodland and they support good populations of breeding wildfowl. The Ballysadare River G63, flowing from Lough Arrow, has a steep waterfall near its mouth which was impassable to Salmon. A fish pass was built there in the nineteenth century and the river system has since supported very good stocks. The road to Mullaghmore passes through some fine reed beds which surround a good area of open water. In winter this usually has Whooper and Bewick's Swan and considerable numbers of duck. Lissadell (on the north side of Drumcliff Bay G64) also has reed beds and a population of White-fronted Goose.

The coast of Sligo is mostly low-lying. Ballysadare Bay is a large estuary with extensive salt marsh and mud flats. To the north of Sligo town there are a series of sandy bays with good rock pools at intervals and fine sand dunes. At Streedagh Point G65 (WNW of Grange) the bare limestone rock along the shore is exceptionally rich in fossils. The material of the fossils is slightly more resistant to the action of the waves than is the surrounding rock so that the fossils stand out clearly. The most impressive species is Caninia, a coral which at first sight looks very like a cabbage stalk. The limestone, in common with practically all of the limestone of Ireland, is of Carboniferous age, a period when the country enjoyed a tropical climate. The island of Inishmurray is low-lying and mainly peat covered. The bog is rich in Purple Loosestrife and Royal Fern. The island is the most southerly nesting place of the Eider Duck on the west coast.

Barnacle Geese. Plentiful in winter on the west and north coasts. As these geese are in danger of extinction shooting is completely prohibited.

Leitrim

The low ground of Leitrim is dominated by drumlin scenery, most of it being in the southern part of the county. Here the well drained upper parts of the hillocks are either tilled or used as pasture while the valleys are marshy or filled with small lakes. There is a small lowland area at the north-west end of the county but otherwise the scenery is mountainous. The Ben Bulbin range extends from Sligo and two of its finest valleys are in Leitrim. These are Glencar and Glenade G84, both with small areas of woodland and a fine variety of alpine flowers. The most interesting ground in this respect is round about the cliffs and screes facing north at Glenade Lough.

The higher ground is peaty with abundant heather. Forestry plantations are scattered through the county and are composed almost entirely of Norway and Sitka Spruce and Contorta Pine. The heavy soils which cover much of Leitrim have been found to be unsuitable for conventional farming but the conifers grow exceptionally well there and there are exciting possibilities of development of forestry on a very large scale. Blanket Bog is found on the higher mountains west of Manorhamilton G84, a continuation of the Sligo bog.

Lakes are the dominant feature of Leitrim. Lough Allen, the highest of the Shannon lakes is a rather barren water but interesting as an exceptionally large example of a poor lake. Lough Melvin G85 is a rich lake with an interesting fish fauna. Char is plentiful and the Brown Trout is known as the 'Gillaroo' (red lad) on account of its bright red spots. The stomach has thicker walls than that of normal trout. The difference between the Gillaroo and other trout results entirely from the type of feeding and it is not a genetic strain. Poor mountain lakes are numerous in the hills between Glenade and Lough Melvin. The lakes in the south-east of the county are richer. The River Shannon forms the county boundary with Roscommon to the south of Lough Allen and flows through drumlin land. It widens further south into Loughs Boderg and Bofin NO9 which are rich and have some good reed beds and marsh by their shores. The sea coast of Leitrim is only three miles long. It is low and rocky.

Donegal

Donegal falls into two distinct regions. The east is relatively rich, rolling lowland. The west is mountainous and poor for the most part. The lowlands extend over a wide area on either side of a line from Lifford H39 to Letterkenny C11. Richer ground is also found in coastal strips around Loughs Foyle and Swilly. Drumlin regions are found in the extreme south of the county, along Donegal Bay as far west as Killybegs G77, at Mulroy Bay C23 and around Kilmacrenan C12. The drumlins are 'drowned' in Donegal Bay and Mulroy Bay and the hilltops form grassy islands. There are colonies of Common Gull on some of the Mulroy Bay islets.

More than half of the area of Donegal is high land, covered with peaty soil or with blanket bog, much of which has been cut away. These conditions are found in all of the main mountain ranges: the Derryveagh B91, the Blue Stack G98, in the Glencolumbkille region G58 and the Slieve Snacht Hills C43 of the Inishowen peninsula. An area of 5,660 acres to the south-east of Dunlewy Lough B91 is owned by An Taisce, it is typical of the mountain bogland community and will be preserved as such. In Glencolumbkille experiments are in progress in developing the mountain soil for intensive market vegetable production and to increase the numbers of sheep which can be reared. Where the bog is drained and fertilized plants such as clovers grow and the typical bog plants like Bog Asphodel disappear. The Glenveagh Deer Forest, in the mountains around Lough Beagh C02 has one of the finest herds of Red Deer in the country. The 'forest' – heathery slopes with relatively little woodland – is completely fenced in but the area is so large that the deer live under completely natural conditions. Much of the woodland is native. At Gartan Lough C01 the Donegal Vocational Education Committee owns land and it is expected that a Field Study Centre will be established there. In general the flora of Donegal has more in common with that of Kerry and west Galway than with the neighbouring counties. Plants such as St Patrick's Cabbage and Royal Fern are common. Dryas is found on Muckish Mountain B92.

On account of the strong winds and shallowness of the soil in many places trees are scarce though the turf cutting in many places shows the stumps of the trees of prehistoric forests. The Ards Forest on a peninsula in the south-western part of Sheep Haven C03 includes some native woodland. Trees planted before State afforestation began in 1930 include the Cork Oak which is a Mediterranean species and fine specimens of Monterey Pine and Macrocarpa. The climate is very mild there and allows southern species to thrive. The forests through the county consist mainly of Sitka Spruce and Contorta Pine. The largest are at Barnesmore H08, Garranbane Hill H09 and around Lough Derg H07. There is an interesting sand dune plantation in Donegal Bay to the west of Laghy G97 and some long-established woodland around Lough Eske G98 which includes Scots Pine and Red Cedar.

The larger lakes of Donegal: Derg H07, Eske G98 and those in the Derryveagh Mountains B91 are all poor but have good stocks of Salmon and Sea Trout. Nearly all of the small lakes, especially those in the mountains and in the Rosses B71 are also poor. These lakes mostly run through short rivers to the sea, the main exception being Lough Derg which flows to the Foyle. Sessiagh Lake (just north of Ballymore C03) is interesting in having a rich stock of planktonic animals and producing large Brown Trout, a curious feature in a lake which, from its position in a bog area, should be poor. The Red Throated Diver nests in one or two of the lakes in the north of the county. This is the only region in Ireland where it is found in summer since it and the other Divers are normally winter visitors. The Diver is strictly an aquatic bird and walks on land only with difficulty. It therefore nests within a few feet of the water's edge. This would be impossible in tidal water so that the bird must go inland to nest but it usually flies to the sea for its food. In the south of the county, at Ballyshannon G96, the River Erne enters the sea. It has been dammed for electricity generating and the dam incorporates a Salmon pass and an Elver ladder. Elvers are also caught at the dam and transported overland to the higher reaches of the river system. The district north of Ballyshannon has a large number of small rich drumlin lakes.

The coast of Donegal is very long and provides excellent examples of all kinds of coastal communites. Most of the rivers have long, muddy estuaries which are sheltered and have good populations of wintering duck and wading birds. One of the best places for winter birdwatching is the lagoon between the Inch peninsula C32 and the mainland. There are many splendid sandy beaches with sand dunes: Rosapenna C13, Portnoo, east of Dunmore Head B69 and Portsalon C23 are amongst the best known. There are numerous areas of cliff scenery. Slieve League G57, reaching a height of over 1,900 feet, has a very interesting alpine flora on its northern slopes. The Chough is common in the Glencolumbkille region. Horn Head C04 is the most important seabird colony. Malin Head C35 is the most northerly point of the Irish mainland and is an excellent headland for the study of migrating birds of all kinds. On good days in spring and autumn many thousands fly past.

A number of the islands, including Rathlin O'Byrne G47 and Inishtrahull C46, have breeding Eider Duck.

Tory Island B84 which has been inhabited since prehistoric times and has interesting archaelogical remains, is a good point for migrating birds. Malin Head and Tory have bird observatories established. Aran Island B61, one of the largest islands on the coast, has a stock of breeding Rainbow Trout in Lough Shore. These trout have been introduced or have escaped in many parts of the country but rarely become established as a breeding species. Grey Seal breed on Aran.

Limpet and Barnacle. Two kinds of animal which have developed streamlined shells and hold firmly to rocks, successfully colonising the exposed area between high and low tides.

The western part of the county has much in common with the neighbouring east Donegal: fairly fertile lowlands with peaty soil on the higher ground. To the east of the River Roe C61 there is a lowland strip of drumlin country and then the land rises steeply in the Sperrin Mountains to form the western edge of the Antrim Basalt plateau. Most of this ground is contained in County Antrim. It is of relatively recent geological age, the Mesozoic Era, very much later than the Carboniferous and older rocks which underly most of the country. The basalt rock was volcanic in origin and poured out over the existing land from great fissures in the earth. It is a basic rock, rich in lime, and therefore weathers to form a rich soil in contrast to the igneous rocks in other parts of Ireland which are acid and deficient in lime. The higher ground of the basalt hills is covered by blanket bog which extends from near the north coast to south of Carn Hill C70. There has been extensive afforestation on the higher ground of these hills. The eastern slopes are gentler than the western and the land drops gradually towards the fertile valley of the Bann and the northwestern corner of Lough Neagh. Spring Hill house, near Moneymore H88, has good parkland and is a National Trust property. The city of Derry itself is closely built over, with little in the way of open spaces. The River Foyle is relatively clean and Salmon can pass through it.

There are rather few lakes in the county. Altnaheglish Forest, to the northwest of Mullaghmore C70, includes a poor mountain lake. There are some small, rich lakes to the south of Kilrea C91. Lough Beg H99, lying in the raised bog, is an excellent place for waterfowl in winter. Very large numbers of Tufted Duck, Pochard, Shoveler,

Wigeon, Teal and Mallard are found. It is a shallow lake, making it ideal for birds like the Tufted Duck which dive for food on the bottom. The Lough Neagh shore in the county is flat with extensive reed beds and fen. An interesting orchid, the Threefold Lady's Tresses, is fairly common around much of Lough Neagh and on the Bann banks but is extremely rare elsewhere in Ireland and almost unknown elsewhere in Europe. It is widely distributed in North America. The largest Eel fishery in the country is on the River Bann where the Lough Neagh eels are caught by the ton at traps at Toome H99 and Coleraine C83 on dark autumn nights.

The greater part of the coast of Derry runs along Lough Foyle and is mostly low-lying with extensive mudbanks at low tide. One of the most interesting parts is the Magilligan C63, a great triangle of flat land, raised from the sea shore as the land rose up following the Ice Age. It is the most extensive tract of 'raised beach' in the country but traces of the beach can be found in many places north of a line from Arklow Head in County Wicklow to Rosses Point in Sligo. The Magilligan has long sandy beaches, sand dunes and swamp. There are cliffs with some breeding seabirds between Portrush and Portstewart C83.

Antrim

Antrim offers a wide variety of conditions from the heavily industrialized city of Belfast to remote glens, sea cliffs and lake shore. In Belfast the River Lagan is seriously polluted and is one of the few rivers in the country which Salmon cannot ascend. The city offers in the Ulster Museum a very well kept display of Irish fauna and flora. As in Dublin there are good regions for bird-watching within the city in particular the Duncrue Street Marsh in the heart of the dockland where duck and waders come in winter.

The county is almost completely underlain by basalt, which lies on top of chalk. The ground is low and fertile towards the west and south but rises to the east to form the magnificent highlands and glens. Ballycastle Forest D13 has been opened as a forest park. Glenarm Forest D21 has natural Ash with Japanese Larch, Norway Spruce and Hemlock Spruce. There are large highland forests also at Carn Hill D38 and west of Browndod D29 and a fine lowland wood on the shores of Lough Neagh to the west of Shane's Castle. Fallow Deer may be seen there. Portglenone Forest C90, containing Spruces, Pines, Japanese Larch, Alder and Poplar, was planted largely to cover spoil heaps made on the banks of the Bann during drainage operations in the 1930's.

The Glens of Antrim, running eastwards from the high land to the sea are famous for their scenery and have fine upland floras. A number of alpine plants are common and there are forests of native Oak. Cliffs and steep scree slopes are plentiful. The finest are in Glenariff D22 and Glendun D23. Inland of Garron Point D22 there is a high plateau of bogland, mostly over 1,000 feet. The area is devoid of trees and roads and is a breeding ground for Curlew, Dunlin, Redshank, Golden Plover and Black-headed and Lesser Black-backed Gull.

Lough Neagh lies more within Antrim than any of the other four counties which touch its edges. The shores are low-lying and have little cover. Apart from the Eel, mentioned in the section on Derry, the most interesting fish is the Pollan which is plentiful enough to form the basis of a commercial net fishery. Lough Neagh is the only water in Ireland where it is worth catching for food. Many species of duck nest on the lake but the most interesting bird there is the Great Crested Grebe which is present in unusually large numbers. Lough Beg D99 has already been mentioned and there are a number of smaller lakes in the county: rich ones such as Portmore Lough J16 and Stonyford J27 and poor mountain lakes such as those on the Garron Plateau.

The Antrim coast has some of the finest cliff scenery in Ireland. The best known is the 'amphitheatre' of the Giant's Causeway C94 where the columns of basalt rock give a fantastic ribbed appearance to the cliff faces. At Fair Head Buzzard breed and the Golden Eagle nested in recent years and may well come back again. There are seabird cliffs on the north coast and at the Gobbins on Islandmagee J49. Larne Lough D40 and Belfast Lough J38 provide sheltered bays with mud flats. Portrush C84 and Whitepark Bay D04 among other places have beaches and sand dunes. Rathlin D15 is an excellent bird island.

Down

The dominant feature of Down is the drumlin land which forms a wide band extending from the north and east coasts to the Armagh border. Belfast, to the east of the Lagan, extends into the county. The Kinnegar, near Sydenham, is an area of mud flat within the city which is

Gull Chicks. Shortly after hatching young gulls leave their nests and their speckled colouring keeps them well hidden amongst rocks or dried grasses.

visited by wintering sea birds. The drumlin land – seen continuously from the road from Banbridge J14 to Hillsborough J25 is rich, well wooded and has a very neat appearance resulting from the well trimmed hedges. Poorer land is found in a band from Lisburn J26 to Lurgan J05 and through most of the south of the county. The Mourne Mountains provide a splendid range of heathery slopes with deep valleys. These mountains, though formed of granite rock similar to the Wicklows, have quite a different appearance since they are very much younger and have not been smoothed to the same extent. Blanket bog is found on the Mournes and on Slieve Croob J34.

Most of the forestry plantations are found around the Mournes though there are small ones also at Hillsborough and to the north of Newtownards J47. The low ground of Rostrevor Forest J11 has Oak wood with Lawson Cypress, Hemlock Spruce, Redwood and Cryptomeria. Tollymore Forest Park, At Bryansford J33 has been a public park since 1955. It has particularly good stands of European Larch with Oak, Beech and Douglas Fir. There is also a large arboretum with a fine collection of rare trees. Pine Marten have been seen there. Red Deer are found at Mountalt, south of Ballynahinch J35.

Most of the drainage of the county is carried by the Bann J14 which rises in the Mourne Mountains and the Lagan J26 which comes from Slieve Croob. Both begin their lives as poor mountain streams but become enriched as they pass through the drumlin land. To the east and south short rivers run to the sea, most of them rather poor. Small lakes are fairly plentiful in the drumlin land but less so than in Monaghan and Cavan. There are good poor lakes in the Mournes and a large Reservoir at Silent Valley J32. Downpatrick Marsh J44 was an excellent place for wintering waterfowl but drainage has reduced the area of suitable ground.

On the coast Strangford Lough provides one of the most interesting regions. Like Clew Bay it is 'drowned' drumlin country and the tips of the submerged hills stand out as numerous islands. In winter Wigeon and Brent Goose are plentiful at the Newtownards end. Gulls nest on Roe Island near Killinchy J56 and there are scattered colonies of terns. There is a wildfowl reserve at Strangford Lough. The Copeland Islands J58 have nesting Shearwater and other seabirds and have been studied intensively for many years. They are also a good point for migrating birds in spring and autumn. St John's Point J53 is another good bird migration headland. The islands of Carlingford Lough J20 have tern colonies. Dundrum Bay J43 has a large area of reed beds backed by salt marsh and lagoon.

Louth

In spite of being the smallest county in Ireland Louth offers a good variety of conditions. Dundalk and Drogheda are sizeable towns with extensive built-up areas and industrial complexes leading to a degree of river pollution. Most of the land is flat and low and relatively rich, there are many large houses with extensive parkland around them. Mellifont Cistercian Abbey at Collon O08 has a particularly good area of woodland in its grounds. The eastern part of the county just includes some drumlin land. The Carlingford J11 peninsula provides the only ground above one thousand feet and with it the only proper hill pasture and peat. Some of the typical mountain plants such as Least Willow and Roseroot are found there. Forest in the county is mainly confined to the Carlingford Mountains. The Ravensdale Forest, in the deep valley where the Dundalk to Newry road runs, contains Douglas Fir, Larch, Spanish Chestnut and the common conifers.

All of the drainage of Louth runs to the Irish Sea. There are several such rivers: the Creggan H91, the Fane J00, the Glyde and the Dee N99. They are slow-flowing lowland streams with good stocks of Salmon, Trout and coarse fish. The Boyne and its tributary the Mattock O07, rich rivers with well wooded banks in places, form the southern boundary of the county. The Glyde runs through a good reed swamp downstream of Castlebellingham O09. On the Carlingford peninsula there are poor and swift-flowing mountain streams. There are no proper lakes but some large rich ponds in many of the estates.

The coast is long and mostly low-lying, though steep but without actual cliffs at Carlingford. There are fisheries for Mussel and Whelk in Carlingford Lough and Dundalk Bay. Clogherhead O18 has low cliffs and rock pools. Elsewhere there are sandy beaches and muddy shores. Lurgan Green, a little to the south of Black Rock J00 is a good area for wintering duck and wading birds with occasional visits from Barnacle Goose. The Boyne Estuary south of Baltray O17 and Dundalk Harbour J00 have extensive mud flats and salt marsh.

Meath

The typical land of County Meath is gently undulating and exceedingly rich, providing the best grazing pasture in the country. Large estates with good parkland are numerous and there are many small woods with broad-leaved trees. There is a large area of esker gravel with a limestone flora south and east of Trim N85. On account of the value of the land for agriculture Meath is the most artificial county in Ireland. Apart from small areas of acid bogland to the north-east of Kells N77 and on the hills east of Collon N98 all of the land has been intensively farmed for thousands of years. The marvellous variety and importance of ancient cemetries, royal seats, castles and churches shows the importance of the area since Neolithic times. There are woods of Hazel and Holly on the hills to the west of the county and the Grey Squirrel is fairly common in these. Forestry plantation is limited and based entirely on old demesnes.

The drainage of most of the county flows to the River Boyne. Within Meath this is a rich, lowland river with many stretches of flood plain with a fine growth of Yellow Flag and reed beds. The Boyne's main tributary, the Kells Blackwater N87 is smaller, not so rich and swifter. Salmon are plentiful in the system. The eastern parts of the county are drained by the Nanny O06 and Devlin O16 Rivers, both rich and fairly slow flowing. There are two canals in the county: the Royal N64 in the south and the Boyne Canal which bypasses various rapids of the main river. A convenient point to see it is at Oldbridge (south of Tullyallen O07). It has been out of use for many years and is an excellent stretch of still, calm water with woodland on its banks. Ten miles of the canal are owned by An Taisce.

Lakes are few. The largest, Lough Sheelin N48, is a rich limestone lake with a very high production of fish. It is being developed with great success by the Inland Fisheries Trust as a Brown Trout lake. Development in

cases such as this involve the removal of Pike and Perch on a large scale. Rich lakes are in fact more suitable for the latter fish than they are for trout so that the preservation of trout in them requires artificial control. Other lakes are Whitewood, to the northwest of Nobber N88 and Lough Bane, Lough Glass North and White Lake, all on the county border in N57. White Lake is very deep, rich and completely landlocked. It has an artificial stock of Rainbow Trout and a very large population of Crayfish. Lough Glass has a good swamp at its northern end with a colony of Black-headed Gull which nest on tussocks of rushes surrounded by water. Mallard nest close to the gulls and probably benefit from this since the gulls chase away predators.

The coast of Meath is short. Along the Boyne estuary, east of Drogheda O17 there are good mud flats and duck and wading birds are plentiful in winter. Mussels are caught in large quantities at Mornington O17. The east coast of the county is low with sand dunes and sandy beaches. The River Nanny enters the sea at Laytown O17 through a short estuary with mud flats, salt marsh and reed beds. There are occasional outcrops of rock with rock pools as at Gormanston O16.

This ends the list of coastal counties. The inland ones, beginning at Tyrone and taking a zig-zag line from county to county southwards are treated in the next section.

Ermine Moth. Like the majority of moths the ermines fly at night and rest in the daytime.

11 THE INLAND COUNTIES

Tyrone

Tyrone is almost entirely a hilly county with rough pastures. The larger towns, such as Omagh H47 and Dungannon H86 are set in the richer parts and have good parkland around them. The lower hills are covered in glacial drift material of various kinds while the high ground, typically with gentle slopes and little in the way of cliffs, is clothed with blanket bog. The Sperrin Mountains H95 to the north, Mullaghcarn H58 in the centre and Fivemiletown H44 in the south are examples. There are large forests on Mullaghcarn, at Oughtmore H78 and on the eastern Sperrins to the north of Carnanelly H99. Baronscourt Demesne, a National Trust property to the southwest of Newtown Steward H34 has fine woodland, surrounding a large lake which contains Roach amongst other fishes. There is also a herd of Sika Deer. At Caledon Forest H74 Fallow Deer are plentiful and there is a herd of Red Deer interbred with Canadian Caribou.

Apart from Lough Neagh, which is mentioned under other counties, the lakes of Tyrone are generally small and poor. There are several in the hills between Mulderg and Carrickmore H57 and one, Lough Fea H78 to the east of the county. In the richer drumlin land to the south there are a few small, rich lakes such as those at Augher H55 and to the north of Minterburn H75. The Blackwater H75, flowing into Lough Neagh, is a rich, lowland river but most of the drainage of the county flows northwards to the Foyle by poor mountain streams, liable to sudden floods after wet weather. The Mourne H39 and the Glenelly H59 are examples. These rivers carry good stocks of trout and Salmon. The Foyle is tidal north of Strabane H39 and flows through a low flood plain, contained in places by embankments. This ground is rich in wading birds and has a number of good reed swamps.

Fermanagh

Rich land and lakes dominate the county. Practically all of the low-lying land is covered with glacial gravels. The fields are enclosed by hedges and there is fine parkland in most regions. In particular Florencecourt, a National Trust property on the south side of Lough Macnean Lower H03, has excellent parks and woods and is interesting as the place of origin of a variety of Common Yew known as the Irish Yew. The first known specimens were found in the mountains nearby, were planted in the estate and cuttings have been very widely distributed in parks and gardens. There are caves at Florencecourt and at Kesh H16. Blanket bog is widely distributed on the higher ground, covering all of the hills to the south of Lower Lough Erne and on the southern border of the county. Smaller areas are found to the east and west of Tempo H34.

The Erne system takes all of the drainage of the county. There are some small, poor lakes in the hills south of Lower Lough Erne but in general the lakes and rivers are set in a limestone basin and are rich. Lough Melvin G95 crosses the border but has already been mentioned in the Leitrim section. Lough Erne itself is an exceptionally interesting and varied stretch of water. The upper lake is a maze of land and water: low hills separate small lakes from each other or appear as islands. Reed beds are plentiful but there are many points where pasture extends to the edge of the water. The hills are well wooded in places. Breeding birds are abundant: Common Tern, Black-headed Gull and Common Gull nest on many of the islands. Great Crested Grebe, Dabchick, Coot and Moorhen are common and there are various species of duck. In winter many more duck and wading birds come in.

The Upper Lake flows to the Lower by a few miles of broad, slow river. The Lower is very much more open but is well supplied with islands in its eastern section. An interesting breeding bird is the Common Scoter, a diving duck which spends the winter in coastal waters but comes inland to breed. The smaller islands of the Upper Lake have interesting plant life, usually very luxuriant with a great deal of native woodland. There are several large forestry plantations around the lake, as to the east of Monea H14 where the lake shore is easily accessible by road. The hills above the southern shore are steep and have many fine cliffs. Those at Poulaphouca are the best known botanically and offer a number of alpine plants. Two interesting species of fish in the Erne are the Roach which was introduced recently and the Pollan which is a member of the early post-glacial fauna.

Armagh

Armagh is largely a drumlin county with rich land and low hills. It is a major centre for horticulture and produces in particular apples and roses. An interesting development now in progress is the merging of the two towns Portadown and Lurgan J05 to form a new city called Craigavon. The increasing population will give

Irish Yew. A variety of the Common Yew which is a native Irish tree. The variety is very popular in parks and gardens.

rise to more sewage which, even though thoroughly treated, will act as fertillizer in Lough Neagh and may cause its waters to deteriorate in quality. The lake is at present being intensively studied so that any effects will be noticed in good time. The south of the county rises in places, the highest point being Slieve Gullion J02 at 1,893 feet. Slieve Gullion and the nearby peaks are capped by blanket bog. There is good parkland and a forest park in the grounds of Gosford Castle, near Markethill H94. The main region of forestry plantation is on Slieve Gullion. There is a belt of raised bog, edged by fen, on the shores of Lough Neagh.

The drainage of the county in the northern part flows to Lough Neagh by the Blackwater H74 and the Bann J05, both rich lowland streams. The disused Ulster Canal H74 runs beside the Blackwater for some distance and in the east of the county the Bann is joined to Carlingford Lough J11 by the Newry Navigation which has also been abandoned as a shipway. In the south of the county the rivers flow into Dundalk Bay. They are poorer streams than those in the north. The Armagh shore of Lough Neagh has extensive fenland and a number of islands. Elsewhere the lakes of Armagh are small, rich ones lying in the drumlin country. There are several good examples to the south of Keady H83. On the northern slopes of Slieve Gullion there is a large reservoir with poor water. To the south of Newry J02 the river is tidal, running between rather steep banks and separated from the road by the ship canal.

Monaghan

Monaghan is the most uniform of the counties of Ireland,

practically all of it being drumlin country, a succession of small hills which cause the rivers and roads to twist hither and thither. The major exception to the rule is in the Slieve Beagh hills H54 which are covered with heather and blanket bog. Apart from this the land in general is rich and well drained with numerous hedges between the fields. The low ground between the hills is either marshy or filled with reed-fringed lakes large and small. There has been extensive forestry plantation to the north-east of Cootehill H61 with Norway and Sitka Spruces and Scots Pine but with some Oak and Ash. The forest at Castleshane H73 is mainly of Norway Spruce but has belts of Sycamore, Oak and Elm with some Beech.

The eastern part of the county drains into the Irish Sea by the River Fane, flowing through Muckno Lake H81. This is a beautiful rich lake, well wooded in places and with extensive reed beds. Great Crested Grebe and many other water birds nest there. To the west the lakes and rivers flow westwards through the Annalee River to the Erne system. The lakes on the Erne System have a rich variety of coarse fish and stocks of Eel of exceptional size. The northern rivers flow to Lough Neagh. The disused Ulster Canal H63 was built to connect Lough Erne to Lough Neagh but rarely contained enough water to permit the easy passage of barges.

Cavan

The typical Cavan land is similar to Monaghan – drumlins, surrounding small lakes and marshes. The well-drained hills give relatively rich pasture and the fields are small and well provided with hedges. This ground prevails over most of the eastern part of the county. To the south the rich Meath pastures cross the county border to form a narrow strip and north of this, from Moynalty N78 to Kilnaleck N49 there is a belt of poor wet pasture and marsh. In the west of the county, on Slieve Russell H22 and the Cuilcagh Mountains H12 there are areas of rather barren blanket bog.

The forests are planted to a considerable extent on demesne land and mixtures of broad-leaved trees are a feature of the county. At Virginia Forest on Lough Ramor N58 the existing Oak wood has been preserved. Bailieboro Forest N69 was established in 1911 and has a good variety of conifers including Norway and Sitka Spruce, Douglas and Silver Firs and Western Red Cedar in addition to broad-leaved species. There are extensive plantations of conifers on the hills at Cootehill H61, Belturbet H31 and Killashandra H30 which come down to the lake shores. Spruces are the main species used. The Grey Squirrel is well established in the county.

Cavan is richly provided with lakes. Lough Ramor which flows to the Boyne through the Blackwater is large and open with a number of wooded islands. The water is rather poor but Bream are plentiful in it in addition to Brown Trout, Perch and Pike. The northern shore offers a variety of communities including Alder swamps and reed beds. The bird life is not so rich as the lakes on the Erne system but Black-headed Gull, Great Crested Grebe and other waterfowl breed there. Small, reed-fringed lakes are abundant in the drumlin regions. Many of these have breeding Great Crested Grebe besides Coot, Moorhen, Mallard and Tufted Duck. The types of nesting birds depend largely on the size of the lake – Tufted Duck and Great Crested Grebe are absent from the smallest. These lakes are also very rich in fish life with Bream, Rudd, Perch and Pike and offer a great variety of aquatic insects. The finest Cavan lakes are those on the Erne and its tributaries. The river, flowing north from Lough Gowna N39 floods the drumlin country between Killashandra and Butler's Bridge H41 making a maze of small lakes wandering amongst the hills. In places they are edged by reed swamp, in others firm pasture land goes down to the water's edge. These lakes can best be explored by boat but there are roads linking up the various peninsulas. They are relatively rich lakes and support large populations of fish and waterfowl. In the south of the county Lough Sheelin N48, already mentioned under Co. Meath, drains through the Inny River into the Shannon.

Longford

Most of the southern half of Longford is rich, lowland pasture, continuing from Meath and Westmeath. North of a line from Granard N38 to Newtown Forbes N18 the land is poorer, a continuation of the belt of poor wet land from Cavan. Along the northern border of the county the drumlin land of Cavan extends southwards to form a narrow strip. In the west the raised bog appears and extends to the county border on the River Shannon. The Lough Ree shore is relatively rich pasture. All in all Longford is scarcely a natural entity but offers instead pieces of land more typical of each of the surrounding counties.

As in Cavan and other midland counties there are Spruce and broad-leaved plantations on the old demesne grounds, as at Ballymahon N15 in the Inny valley and around Lough Gowna N39. The Grey Squirrel was in-

Colonisation. The dog daisy is one of the first plants to invade bare ground, in this case the spoil heap from arterial drainage works.

troduced to County Longford from America in 1911 and is now well established there. The Red Squirrel is also common in places.

Apart from the Shannon the Inny N37 and the Camlin N17 are the main rivers. The Inny has been very thoroughly cleaned and straightened in the course of Arterial Drainage work and presents a canal-like appearance over much of its length with steep sides and rather barren banks. The recolonisation of the spoil heaps by plants will make an interesting study. The southern shores of Lough Gowna, lying in the poor pasture region of the county, are well wooded and there is one large island in the lake. The northwestern county boundary runs through a series of typical drumlin lakes. On the Shannon Lough Forbes N08 is a relatively small and open lake in the raised bog. The main river meanders through the bog until it opens into Lough Ree. The northern lake shores are flat and marshy but further south they become drier and are backed by low hills. There are several large islands which have few or no inhabitants but are grazed by cattle. The numerous small islands have natural scrub vegetation, often with a fringe of Yellow Loosestrife and a variety of reeds and rushes. The low-lying ones have colonies of Black-headed Gull and Common Tern. The Royal Canal N07 runs through the south of the county to the Shannon at Cloondara N07 with a branch to Longford town N17. An interesting temporary development on the Shannon is the warm water coming from Lanesborough N06 power station. It raises the temperature of the river slightly and provides an attractive breeding place for such fishes as Tench and Bream.

Roscommon

Roscommon is a large and varied county. It has a central area of rich grazing land. Much of this is unusual in Ireland in being used mainly for sheep. The reason is that a large proportion of the drainage runs underground and there is very little surface water. Cattle need open water to drink but sheep are able to get enough moisture from the grass. Stone walls rather than hedges as field boundaries are a characteristic even of the richer parts of the county.

There are three large state forests of which the most important and interesting is Ballyfarnon which includes the Rockingham Estate on the eastern shore of Lough Key G80. This has been opened as a Forest Park. The planted trees include Larch, Spruce, Douglas Fir and Pine but the existing hardwood forest has been preserved and contains Elm, Sycamore, Ash, Beech and Oak.

North of a line from Boyle G80 to Leitrim G90 drumlin land prevails. North-west of Boyle in the Curlew Mountains and on the western side of Lough Gara M79 there is blanket bog. To south and east of the county there are large areas of raised bog – in the valleys of the Shannon and its tributary, the Suck. The raised bog is being exploited on a large scale.

The drainage of Roscommon all flows into the Shannon, either to the main river or to the Suck. Both of these are rich, lowland rivers within the county. They flood extensively in winter and the floodlands – called 'callows' – are rich in birdlife. Lough Gara is a rather poor, open lake set amidst bogland. Lough Key is rich and plentifully supplied with islands, some of which have natural scrub vegetation. Lough Ree occupies most of the east of the county. The sheltered bays, many with reed swamps, are the most productive parts. As the lake is relatively shallow it has a good population of duck in summer and winter. Lough Funshinagh M95 has a great expanse of dense reed beds and is an excellent spot for duck and wading birds in winter. A roughly triangular area bounded by Drumsna M09, Elphin M88 and Strokestown M98 has a large number of small lakes. Some are easily accessible but others are far from roads and dwellings and have not been fully explored.

Westmeath

Most of the Westmeath land is rich. The county is typically hilly though seldom rising to much more than 500 feet. Rich glacial gravels are prevalent and the road from Kinnegad N54 to Athlone N04 follows the raised ground of an esker ridge. Small Hazel woods with Beech, Sycamore, Holly and other trees are plentiful in the region and the Grey Squirrel is common. There are many well wooded estates. Raised bog makes small appearances to the south of Athlone and south-east of Tyrrellspass N43. Marshes are widely scattered in low-lying ground and there is a fine area of fen and reedswamp between the racecourse at Mullingar N45 and the shores of Lough Ennel. In summer Grasshopper Warbler and Whinchat are common there.

Afforestation has taken place mainly on demesne lands though poor ground in the form of bog or cutaway bog has been used in the south of the county. The most interesting forest is Mullaghmeen, on the south side of Lough Sheelin N48. This is the biggest broad-leaved plantation in the country with a great deal of Beech as well as Corsican and Scots Pines. Lough Owel Forest N45 and Baronstown Forest to the west of Lough Iron N36 have Norway Spruce interspersed with groups of Oak.

The water of the county flows to the Shannon. In the west it goes directly to Lough Ree and to the main river, to the north it flows by the Inny N37 to Lough Ree and to the south by the Brosna N12. The Royal Canal, supplied with water from Lough Owel N45 cuts the county roughly in two from south-east to north-west. In the east of the county some relatively small rivers flow to the Boyne. Small, reed-fringed lakelets with rich water are fairly plentiful but the typical Westmeath lakes are large ones. Lough Ree lies on the western border but differs little from the Longford section. Hare Island

N04 has some fine woodland. The other lakes are centred around Mullingar and Castlepollard N47. In spite of lying close to each other they are very different in character.

Lough Owel is mainly a spring-fed lake with very clear and lime-rich water. Half a mile to the east of it is the Scraw Bog, a long narrow lake covered by dense vegetation. It is an acid bog but unusually rich in nutrients and has a very interesting flora with sedges, horsetails and a rare Cotton Grass. Lough Derravaragh N46 is fed by the rather acid River Inny and has brownish water. In recent years drainage work has lowered the level of Derravaragh and other lakes in the region and they are developing new shore lines. Loughs Owel and Ennel N34 have islands with breeding duck. From the point of view of bird-watching Lough Glore L47 (ENE of Castlepollard) is probably the most productive. It is less than a mile long but is so shallow that its entire bed has a dense growth of weeds, supporting a very rich fauna. For this reason it attracts a far greater concentration of duck and other waterfowl than do the larger and deeper lakes nearby. All of the Mullingar lakes have very good stocks of fish: Brown Trout, Pike and Perch in particular. Char were found in Lough Owel until the nineteenth century but have not been seen since. They were exceptionally large, regularly reaching 2 lb. It is possible that they still survive there.

Offaly

Raised bog is the dominant type of land in Offaly. From the Shannon to the Kildare border there are great expanses of flat bogland or pasture on cut-away bog. Most of the ground in between is rich and well wooded and near the Shannon there are low hills of limestone gravel in places. Hills are a little more pronounced towards the north in the region of Clare N23 where the esker ridges are prominent and in the south where the Slieve Bloom Mountains N20 rise to 1,600 feet.

Natural Oak wood with the usual undergrowth of Holly and other trees is found on the private plantation of Clonad Wood, about 7 miles south of Tullamore N32 on the road T9. Kinnitty Forest, which covers large areas on the Slieve Blooms has Contorta Pine, Japanese Larch and Sitka Spruce. At Clonsast Bog, near Clonbulloge N62, there is an interesting experimental forest. A strip of cut-away bog a mile in length and thirty yards wide has been divided into a series of half-acre plots, each planted with a different tree species. There are three Poplars, three Spruces, three Pines, three Firs, two Larches, Lawson Cypress, Western Red Cedar and Hemlock Spruce. The planting took place in 1955.

The bog is being exploited on a very large scale but there are still many places where it can be seen under more or less natural conditions. Nearly all of the main roads in the district skirt the bog rather than going through it. The road from Edenderry N63 through Tullamore to Cloghan N01, however, runs mainly through the bog and gives a very good impression of the nature of the land. The only objects which break the horizon are the factories and generating stations which use the turf and lines of Spruce, Pine and Birch which have been planted in places.

Offaly is the watershed between the Shannon and the Boyne, with most of the water running to the Shannon through the River Brosna N12. In spite of running through so much bog the Brosna is a relatively rich river, having collected plenty of lime in its passage through the Westmeath land. The Grand Canal N32 runs east and west through the county and also contains rich water. Lough Boora N11 is a bog lake. Pallas Lake N21 on the other hand is a very rich water. It is land-locked and has been stocked with Rainbow Trout. In the west Offaly is bounded by the Shannon which is broad and slow and bordered by 'callow' lands which flood in winter. On account of the flooding very few roads go close to the river and the best approach is by boat. Banagher N01 is a good centre, lying just upstream of the Friar's Island region where canals have been dug to bypass rapids on the main river. This region has a large population of duck and some White-fronted Goose in winter. The most easterly of the canals has been long abandoned and its banks have a good growth of Ash, Hawthorn and other bushes.

Kildare

The typical Kildare land is rich with gently rolling plains. Post-and-rail fences enclose stud farms where many of the finest horses are reared on the fertile land. In this respect it is similar to the rich ground in Limerick and Meath. The large farms have plenty of small areas of woodland. Parkland can be seen at its finest at Castletown, near Celbridge N93 and at Carton, Maynooth N93 both of which have been opened to the public. The Curragh N71 with its well cropped grass is an example of the effects of sheep grazing on esker gravels. Gorse, protected by its sharp, spiny leaves, is the only shrub which manages to survive. As in County Roscommon the shortage of open water makes cattle raising impractica-

Dragonflies. Adult dragonflies live and mate on the land but the eggs are laid in water and the young develop there, taking one or two years to complete the cycle.

ble. The forest at Moore Abbey, Monasterevin N61 has well established stands of Ash, Douglas Fir and Norway Spruce and some unusual mixtures planted in recent years. These include alternating bands of Norway Spruce and Oak and other species are Beech and Silver Fir in mixture, Douglas Fir, Scots Pine and natural Ash.

One of the largest fens in Ireland is found near Newbridge N81. Attempts were made to drain it recently but it is expected that parts of it at least will remain unchanged. Blanket bog, an extension of the Offaly region, lies in the west of the county and can be seen well from the road from Prosperous N82 to Rathangan N61.

In the northwest of the county drainage water flows to the Boyne by a number of tributaries such as the Blackwater N83 and the Boyne itself forms part of the county boundary with Offaly. It is here a rather poor river and carries a heavy burden of peat silt. The Liffey drains the eastern part of Kildare. It leaves the Poulaphouca Reservoir N90 as a rather poor river by the magnificent gorge at Poulaphouca. This deep valley is interesting in being too steep for much grazing to be possible and yet having enough ledges and level places to allow a good growth of plant life. It therefore presents a picture of almost completely natural conditions of vegetation. The river becomes greatly enriched as it passes through the county and over most of its length is a meandering lowland river with reed beds and fertile fields on its banks. The Barrow N60 flows to the south, and as with the Boyne much of its journey takes it through the turf bogs and it is fairly heavily silt laden. There are no proper lakes in the county but a considerable number of small, rich ponds with marshy surroundings. In summer some of these support colonies of Black-headed Gull and have breeding Mallard. In winter they are visited by small parties of duck such as Tufted Duck and Pochard. There is a good selection of these ponds in the region of Punchestown race course N91.

Laois

Laois is mainly a country of rich lowlands, well wooded

and well supplied with hedges. The road from Dublin to Limerick runs through the typical land and also gives examples of some other features. North-east of Portlaoise S49 is the Heath, a rather dry area with gorse in plenty. A few miles to the southwest of the town there is an area of raised bog on both sides of the road, one of a number of small boglands scattered through the county. To the northwest of the road the Slieve Bloom mountains N02 with their cap of peaty soil and extensive forest can be seen.

Forests, based largely on old demesnes, are an important feature of the county. Abbyleix Estate S48, crossed by the Cork road south of the town, has about a thousand acres of privately owned forest. Parkhill Wood, within the estate, is over 300 years old and may contain native Oak woodland besides which it has natural Ash and Birch with Spruces, Lawson Cypress and Scots Pine in plantations. Durrow Forest S37 has natural Ash and Birch in addition to the common conifers. The Slieve Bloom forests cover large areas of mountain side and have mainly Sitka Spruce, Japanese Larch and Contorta Pine. Fallow Deer are common there.

Most of the county is drained by the Nore which is a rich river running through rather flat land. Several of its tributaries, such as the Delour River S29, are mountain streams from the Slieve Blooms. The Delour flows through a beautifully wooded valley. The rest of the drainage flows eastwards to the Barrow and is made up of flat, rich streams. The Barrow branch of the Grand Canal runs to the west of the river southwards from Monasterevin N61. Lakes are very few: Annaghmore Lough N31 lies in the raised bog area and is the largest open water in the county. Ballyfin Lake N30 is smaller and richer.

Tipperary is the largest and most varied of the inland counties. Much of its land is gently rolling, fertile country with a large proportion of tillage. This land is seen at its best in a wide region centred on Cashel S04. The abundance of castles and rich monastic sites is evidence of the long established value of the land. Well wooded estates are numerous but there has been a tendency to enlarge the fields by the removal of hedges and these are comparatively scarce in places. The Rock of Cashel, apart from its fine ruins, is interesting in providing a rocky outcrop of limestone with some steep cliffs.

In contrast to the rich land of the plains two large mountain ranges provide poor hill pasture surmounted by blanket bog. These are the Galty Mountains R82 and the northern slopes of the Knockmealdowns S00. Slievenamon S22 is an outlying mountain of over 2,000 feet and there are several areas of lower hills: Slieveardagh S35, Mauherslieve R86 and the Silvermines R86, the Devilsbit S07 and the Arra Mountains R77, all capped with peaty soil or blanket bog. The Galtys are particularly interesting in having a considerable number of alpine plants, found mainly on the cliffs above the corries on the north-facing slopes. Fallow Deer are common. There is a large area of raised bog to the east of Urlingford S26 and smaller patches at Carriganorig M90.

Afforestation has been undertaken on a great many of the hill slopes. Both sides of the Galty Mountains, the northern slopes of the Knockmealdowns, the southern part of Slievenamon and the hills around Dundrum R94 have woods mainly of Sitka Spruce, Contorta Pine and Larches. The forest around Kilcooley Abbey S25 began as a private forest and was taken over by the

State in the 1930s. It includes long-established woods of Beech, Oak and Ash besides Scots Pine, Norway Spruce and European Larch.

The main lake is Lough Derg which forms most of the western boundary of the county. The lake shore is backed in most places by rich level ground with many large and well wooded estates. Behind this tract the land rises to several hundred feet. One of the most interesting plants is the Juniper which elsewhere in Ireland grows wild as a low, creeping shrub. By Lough Derg it reaches a height of 29 ft. in places. The Yew is also common as a wild tree. A fine wood with both of these species is found on the shore north of the Bounla Islands (WNW of Ballinderry R89). As already mentioned under County Clare the lake is rich in bird life. To the east of Lough Derg there are numerous small, rich lakes with reed beds and Alder groves. The road from Puckaun R88 to Coolbaun R89 passes several of them. Lough Ourna, to the west of the road and half way between Nenagh R87 and Borrisokane R99 is a reserve. It has fine reed beds and many duck in winter and summer including Shoveler and Mallard, there is also a Black-headed Gull colony. North of Lough Derg the Shannon winds through its flood plain, a continuation of the callows of Offaly. South of Ballina R77 the Shannon has been dammed at Parteen Weir (beside Mountpelier R66) and forms a reservoir. The dam diverts the water from the main bed of the river to the power station at Ardnacrusha. There is a large Salmon rearing establishment, owned by the Electricity Supply Board, at Parteen.

Most of the drainage of the county runs to the broad, rich River Suir S04. It has very fertile flood plain and holds good stocks of Salmon, Trout and Eel. Most of the tributaries are rich but those coming off the slopes of the

Galty Mountains are poor streams, liable to sudden flooding. There are several poor lakes in the Corries of the Galtys.

Kilkenny

The fertile land of Kilkenny is found in the lowlands of the valleys of the Nore S54 and by the estuaries of the Barrow and Suir. It is rich land and there are many large, well wooded estates, especially on the Nore. The demesne of Kilkenny Castle S55 is a good example. The higher ground in general is poorer and the uplands have a rather barren appearance. Slieveardagh S35, the hills north and south of Castlecomer S57 and in the south of the county between New Ross S77 and Slievenamon S72

Puff Ball. One of the many species of fungus which live on the decaying leaves of trees in forests.

all present a similar appearance and are thinly populated – all of the major towns lie on the lower ground. The forestry plantations are partly on the high ground and partly based on old demesne lands. The main upland ones are west of Graiguenamanagh S64, south of Inistioge S63, where they clothe the steep valley of the Nore and west of Hugginstown S53. In Inistioge Demesne there is a fine collection of exotic conifers of about 100 years of age. They include some of the earliest specimens of important forest trees to be introduced to the country such as Silver Fir, Redwood and Cedars and there is an avenue of Monkeypuzzles.

The Nore and its tributaries take most of the drainage of the county. The main river is broad, slow-flowing and rich like the others in the region. In most places it flows through pasture land but there are areas of reed beds at intervals. Salmon, Trout and Eel are plentiful and Twaite Shad breed downstream of Inistioge. There is little serious pollution. A very interesting plant in the valley is the Autumn Crocus which is abundant in many places on the Nore and its tributaries from Freshford S46 and Callan S44 down to Inistioge. It is found in adjoining counties on the Nore and for a short stretch of the Barrow but is unknown elsewhere in the country.

Kilkenny scarcely qualifies as an inland county since its south-eastern portion is bounded by tidal water of the estuaries of the Suir and Barrow and the Nore itself is tidal as far upstream as Inistioge. There are extensive reed beds along the Suir and on the Barrow, and downstream of Carrick-on-Suir S42 Willow growing has taken place for centuries and supplied the needs of the local basket industry. Among other products Eel traps are made and, baited with fresh Sprat and other sea fish, are used in the estuaries.

The greater part of Carlow is gently undulating, rich lowlands. Much of it is under tillage and the county is an important sugar beet growing region. The land rises towards the east and such towns as Hacketstown S98 and Borris S75 lie surrounded by rather poor soil, derived from the southern extension of the Wicklow granite. The highest point in the county is Mount Leinster S85 and the Blackstairs Mountains S84 to the south of it also exceed a height of 2,000 feet. Blanket bog is found on their higher parts and there are good heather-covered slopes. The main forestry plantations are on the slopes of Mount Leinster.

The northern part of the county is drained by the Slaney, a swift, poor river with good Salmon stocks. The rest of the drainage is based on the Barrow which is a relatively rich lowland river. It carries a heavy burden of peat silt from its tributaries in the Kildare and Offaly bogs and is sometimes heavily polluted in the course of its passage through such towns as Athy S69 and Carlow S77. In spite of this it maintains good stocks of Salmon and other fish. Much of the Barrow is navigable – or was until recently and forms a branch of the Grand Canal – a system of weirs and bypasses with locks is used to allow boats to pass the rapids. Fishing for migrating eels is carried out by the lock keepers who use small nets attached to poles and inserted in the sluices of the lock gates.

There are no proper lakes in the county but a number of large ponds on some big estates. In 1970 one such pond at Oak Park Estate, just north of Carlow was declared a wildlife sanctuary. The estate is one of fine parkland and tillage and is owned by the Agricultural

Institute. The 'lake' is a very rich and shallow water with a large population of Coot and Moorhen as well as Mallard and other duck. It is surrounded by a very large reed bed and there is extensive woodland. The wood was originally a plantation and contains stands of such conifers as Spruce and Pine but it also has Birch, Holly, Alder, Beech and Oak. As a forest it has long been neglected in parts and presents almost completely natural conditions with fallen trees lying and decaying without being removed.

Fritillary Butterfly. Butterflies, feeding on nectar and moving from flower to flower are essential agents in cross-pollination.

BIBLIOGRAPHY

Books marked * are out of print but should be obtainable in the larger libraries.

1. Works covering the whole country

* *The Botanist in Ireland,* R.L. Praeger, Dublin 1934, an invaluable book, giving very detailed information on the distribution of higher plants.

* *Natural History of Ireland,* R.L. Praeger, London 1950.

The Way That I Went, R.L. Praeger, Paperback edition Dublin 1969.

The Sea Anglers' Fishes, M. Kennedy, London 1969.

Ireland's Birds, R.F. Ruttledge, London 1966.

A Guide to Irish Birds, C. Moriarty, Cork 1967.

The Fauna of Ireland, F.J. O'Rourke, Cork 1970, an introduction to the land vertebrates.

2. Regional Works

Flora of Howth, H.C. Hart, Dublin 1887.

* *Flora of the County Donegal,* H.C. Hart, Dublin 1898.

* *Flora of the County Dublin,* N. Colgan, Dublin 1904 (Supplement published by National Museum, Dublin 1961.)

* *Flora of County Kerry,* R.W. Scully, Dublin 1916.

Flora of the North-east Ireland, S.A. Stewart and T.H. Corry, Belfast, 2nd Edition 1938, (Derry, Antrim and Down).

Flora of the County Wicklow, J.P. Brunker, Dundalk 1950.

The Wild Flowers of County Louth, D. Synnott, Dundalk 1970.

An Irish Sanctuary, P.G. Kennedy, Dublin 1953 (Birds of the North Bull Island.)

Birds of Northern Ireland, C.D. Deane, Belfast 1954.

3. Identification

An Irish Flora, D.A. Webb, Dundalk 1953 (and revised editions).

The Concise British Flora in Colour, W. Keble Martin, London 1965.

Collins Pocket Guide to the Seashore, J.H. Barrett and C.M. Yonge, London 1958.

A Field Guide to the Mammals of Britain and Europe, F.H. van den Brink, London 1967.

The Oxford Book of Insects. J. Burton, Oxford 1968.

INDEX

Abies *see* Silver Fir
Abramis *see* Bream
Accipiter *see* Sparrow Hawk
Acer *see* Sycamore
Acrocephalus *see* Sedge Warbler
Actinia *see* Beadlet Anemone
Adiantum *see* Maidenhair
Aesculus *see* Horse Chestnut
Alauda *see* Skylark
Albatross (Diomedea), 89, 108
Alca impennis *see* Great Auk
A. torda *see* Razorbill
Alcedo *see* Kingfisher
Alder (Alnus glutinosa), 39, 47, 52, 54, 141, 156, 169, 173
Allium *see* Wild Garlic
Alnus *see* Alder
Alosa *see* Shad
A. fallax *see* Twaite Shad
Ammophila *see* Marram
Anas acuta *see* Pintail
A. crecca *see* Teal
A. penelope *see* Wigeon
A. platyrhynchos *see* Mallard
A. strepera *see* Gadwall
Ancylastrum *see* River Limpet
Anemone *see* Wood Anemone
Anguilla *see* Eel
Anser albifrons *see* White-fronted Goose
A. anser *see* Grey-lag Goose
Anthus pratensis *see* Meadow Pipit
A. spinoletta *see* Rock Pipit
Anthyllis *see* Kidney Vetch
Apodemus *see* Woodmouse
Apus *see* Swift
Aquila *see* Golden Eagel
Araucaria *see* Monkeypuzzle
Arbutus unedo, 47, 109, 131
Arctic Tern (Sterna macrura), 77
Ardea *see* Heron
Arenaria *see* Irish Sandwort
Argynnis *see* Pearl-bordered Fritillary
Armeria *see* Sea Pink
Asellus *see* Water Louse
Ash (Fraxinus excelsior), 27, 45, 47, 116, 121, 141, 155, 160, 164, 165, 167, 169
Asio *see* Long-eared Owl
Asplenium ruta muraria *see* Wall Rue
A. trichomanes *see* Spleenwort
Astacus *see* Crayfish
Aster *see* Sea Aster
Asterias *see* Starfish
Autumn Crocus (Colchicum autumnale), 171
Aythya ferina *see* Pochard
A. fuligula *see* Tufted Duck
A. marila *see* Scaup

Badger (M. meles) 32, 40, 48
Balanus *see* Barnacle
Balearic Shearwater (P.p. mauretanicus), 90
Bank Vole (Clethrionymys glareolus), 64
Bannackeen *see* Irish Spurge
Barley (Hordeum), 27
Barnacle (Balanus), 78, 79, *138*
Barnacle Goose (Branta leucopsis), 130, *133,* 146
Barn Owl (Tyto alba), 36

Bar-tailed Godwit (Limosa lapponica), 95
Basking Shark (Cetorhinus maximus), 89, 129
Bass (Morone labrax), 86, 100
Bat *see* Leisler's, Long-eared, Pipistrelle
Beadlet Anemone (Actinia equina), *80*
Bear (Ursus arctos), 13, 131
Beech (Fagus sylvatica), 29, 47, 92, 106, 110, 116, 120, 121, 144, 155, 160, 161, 165, 169, 173
Bellis *see* Daisy
Beta *see* Sea Beet
Betula *see* Birch
Bewick's Swan (Cygnus columbianus), 72, 97, 122, 132
Bird's Foot Trefoil (Lotus corniculatus), 43, 75
Birch (Betula), 47, 121, 131, 163, 167, 173
Blackbird (Turdus merula), 18, 35, 42
Black Fly (Simulium), 59
Black Guillemot (Cepphus grylle), 82, 94, 97
Black-headed Gull (Larus ridibundus), 19, 24, 27, 66, 71, 98, 118, 120, 124, 141, 149, 152, 156, 159, 166, 169
Black-tailed Godwit (Limosa limosa), 108
Blackthorn (Prunus spinosa), 27, 121
Bladder Wrack (Fucus), 78
Blennius *see* Blenny
B. folis *see* Butterfish
Blenny, 86
Bluebell (Scilla non-scripta), 45
Blue Gentian (Gentiana verna), 43, 117
Blue Hare *see* Hare
Blue Tit (Parus caeruleus), 19, 35, 48
Bog Asphodel (Narthecium ossifragum), 39, 56, 135
Bog Cotton *see* Cotton Grass
Bog Violet *see* Great Butterwort
Bracken (Pteridium aquilinum), 15, 37, 47
Bramble (Rubus), 27, 45, 47
Branta bernicla *see* Brent Goose
B. leucopsis *see* Barnacle Goose
Bream (Abramis brama), 10, 62, 110, 156, 157, 159
Brent Goose (Branta bernicla), 94, 95, 112, 145
Brittle Starfish (Ophiuroidea), 80
Briza *see* Quaking Grass
Brooklime (Veronica beccabunga), 21, 61
Brown Hare (Lepus europaeus), 31
Brown Trout (Salmo trutta), 22, 60, 62, 63, 64, 66, 86, 97, 110, 122, 126, 127, 134, 136, 146, 147, 151, 156, 162, 169, 171
Buccinum *see* Whelk
Bucephala *see* Goldeneye
Bufo *see* Natterjack
Bullfinch (P. pyrrhula), 18
Bullrush (Scirpus lacustris), 51, 65, 68

Bunting *see* Reed B., Snow B., Yellowhammer
Burren Green (Calamia tridens), 117
Buteo *see* Buzzard
Buttercup (Ranunculus), 26-28, 52
Butterfish (Blennius pholis), 79
Butterwort *see* Common, B. Great B.
Buzzard (B. buteo), 142

Caddis (Trichoptera), 59, 61
Calamia tridens *see* Burren Green
Calidris alpina *see* Dunlin
C. canutus *see* Knot
Calliostoma *see* Topshell
Caltha palustris *see* Marsh Marigold
Canadian Pondweed (Elodea canadensis), 68
Cancer *see* Edible Crab
Caninia, 132
Canis *see* Wolf
Capella *see* Snipe
Caprimulgus *see* Nightjar
Capsella *see* Shepherd's Purse
Carcinus *see* Shore Crab
Cardium *see* Cockle
Carduelis cannabina *see* Linnet
C. carduelis *see* Goldfinch
Carp (Cyprinus carpio), 62
Castanea *see* Spanish Chestnut
Catstail (Phleum pratense), 27
Cat *see* Wild Cat
Cepphus *see* Black Guillemot
Certhia *see* Tree Creeper
Ceterarch *see* Rusty-back
Cetorhinus *see* Basking Shark
Cervus elephas *see* Red Deer
C. giganteus *see* Irish Deer
C. nippon *see* Sika Deer
Chaffinch (Fringilla coelebs), 18, 34
Chamaecyparis *see* Lawson Cypress
Char (Salvelinus), 66, 97, 103, 111, 124, 134, 162
Charadrius apricarius *see* Golden Plover
C. hiaticula *see* Ringed Plover
Chestnut *see* Horse C., Spanish C.
Chiffchaff (Phylloscopus collybita), 19, 35, 48
Chironomid, 20, 22, 59, 61
Chloris *see* Greenfinch
Chough (P. pyrrhocorax), 82, 103, 112, 119, 137
Chrysanthemum *see* Dog Daisy
Cinclus *see* Dipper
Clustered Alpine Saxifrage (S. nivalis), 131
Clangula *see* Long-tailed Duck
Clethrionomys *see* Bank Vole
Close-flowered Orchid (Neotinea intacta), 43
Clover (Trifolium), 27
Clupea *see* Herring
Coal Tit (Parus ater), 35, 48
Cockle (Cardium), 86, 95
Cocksfoot (Dactylis glomerata), 27
Cod (Gadus morrhua), 89
Colchicum *see* Autumn Crocus
Columbia livia *see* Rock Dove, Pigeon
C. Palumbus *see* Wood Pigeon
Common Butterwort (Pinguicula vulgaris), 39

Common Gull (Larus canis), 19, *67*, 71, 113, 124, 127, 135, 152
Common Sandpiper (Tringa hypoleucos), 71, 96, 97, 122
Common Seal (Phoca vitulina), 89
Common Tern (Sterna hirundo), 71, 77, 111, 118, 124, 152, 159
Conger conger, 80
Contorta Pine (Pinus contorta), 48, 92, 106, 121, 134, 136, 163, 167, 168
Coot (Fulica atra), 21, 24, 69, 70, 93, 97, 118, 152, 156, 173
Coralline (Lithophyllum), 78
Coregonus *see* Pollan
Corixid *see* Waterboatman
Cork Oak (Quercus suber), 136
Cormorant (Phalacrocorax carbo), 24, 71, 77, 82, 83, 87
Corsican Pine (Pinus nigra), 99, 110, 161
Corvus corax *see* Raven
C. frugilegus *see* Rook
C. monedula *see* Jackdaw
Corylus *see* Hazel
Cory's Shearwater (Procellaria diomeda), 90
Cotton Grass (Eriophorum), 52, 56, 101, 162
Crab *see* Edible C., Shore C.
Crabapple (Malus pumila), 121
Crane *see* Heron
Cranefly (Tipula), 27
Crategus *see* Hawthorn
Crawfish (Palinurus vulgaris), 80
Crayfish (Astacus pallipes), 149
Creeping Willow (Salix repens), 75
Crex *see* Corncrake
Crithmum *see* Golden Samphire
Crossleaved Heath (Erica tetralix), 55
Crow *see* Hooded C., Rook
Crowfoot (Ranunculus), 58
Cryptomeria, 144
Cupressus macrocarpa, 136
Curlew (Numenius arquata), 29, 72, 94, 97, 141
Cygnus columbianus *see* Bewick's Swan
C. cygnus *see* Whooper Swan
C. olor *see* Mute Swan
Cynosurus *see* Dogstail
Cyprinus *see* Carp

Dabchick (Podiceps ruficollis), 69-71, 93, 97, 118, 152
Daboecia *see* St. Dabeoc's Heath
Dace (L. leuciscus), 107
Dactylis *see* Cocksfoot
Daisy (Bellis perennis), 18
Daddy-long-legs *see* Cranefly
Dama *see* Fallow Deer
Dandelion (Taraxacum officinale), *16*, 18, 26
Dark Red Helleborine (Epipactis atrorubens), 117
Deer *see* Fallow D., Red D., Sika D.
Deergras (Trichophorum caespitosum), 56
Delichon *see* House Martin
Delphinus *see* Dolphin

Dicrostonyx *see* Lemming
Dipper (C. cinclus), 24, 60, 111
Diver *see* Great Northern D., Red-throated D.
Dog Daisy (Chrysanthemum leucanthemum), 26, *158*
Dogstail (Cynosurus cristatus), 27
Dolphin (D. delphinus), 89
Douglas Fir (Pseudotsuga taxifolia), 110, 144, 146, 156, 160, 165
Dragonfly (Odonata), 52, *73, 165*
Drosera *see* Round-leaved Sundew
Dryas octopetala, *43,* 117, 131, 136
Duck *see* Tufted Duck
Dunlin (Calidris alpina), 95, 141

Earthworm (Lumbricus), 27, 32
Echinoidea *see* Sea Urchin
Edible Crab (Cancer pagurus), 80
Eel (A. anguilla), 22, 60-63, 66, 86, 91, 100, 118, 122, 124, 137, 140, 141, 155, 169, 171, 172
Eelgrass (Zostera marina), 85
Eider (Somateria mollissima), 132, 137
Elm (Ulmus), 116, 121, 155, 160
Elodea *see* Canadian Pondweed
Emberiza citrinella *see* Yellowhammer
E. schoeniculus *see* Reed Bunting
Ephemeroptera *see* Mayfly
Epilobium *see* Willow Herb
Epipactis *see* Dark Red Helleborine
Equisetum *see* Horsetail
Erica cinerea *see* Heather
E. mackaiana *see* Mackey's Heath
E. mediterranea *see* Mediterranean Heath
E. tetralix *see* Crossleaved Heath
Erithacus *see* Robin
Erinaceus *see* Hedgehog
Eriocaulon *see* Pipewort
Eriophorum *see* Cotton Grass
Ermine Moth (Spilosoma), *148*
Eryngium *see* Sea Holly
Esox *see* Pike
Eucalyptus, 106, 110
Euonymus *see* Spindle Tree
Euphorbia *see* Irish Spurge

Fagus *see* Beech
Falco columbarius *see* Merlin
F. tinnunculus *see* Kestrel
Fallow Deer (D. dama), 18, 40, 91, 96, *99,* 102, 109, 121, 141, 150, 167, 168
Felis *see* Wildcat
Fieldfare (Turdus pilaris), 35
Filipendula *see* Meadowsweet
Flagger *see* Yellow Flag
Flounder (Pleuronectes flesus), 24, 86, 100, 114
Flycatcher *see* Pied F., Spotted F.
Forget-me-not (Myosotis), 52
Fox (V. vulpes), 18, 32, 40, 91
Fratercula *see* Puffin
Fraxinus *see* Ash

Freshwater Shrimp (Gammarus), 22
Fringilla *see* Chaffinch
Fritillary (Argynnis), *173*
Frog (Rana temporaria), 13, 53, 54
Fuchsia magellanica, 121
Fucus *see* Bladder Wrack
Fulica *see* Coot
Fulmar (Fulmarus glacialis), 82, 83, *84*, 94, 97, 102

Gadus morrhua *see* Cod
G. pollachius *see* Pollack
Gadwall (Anas strepera), 113
Gallinula *see* Moorhen
Gammarus *see* Freshwater Shrimp
Gannet (Sula bassana), 77, 82, 83, 108, 112
Garlic *see* Wild Garlic
Garrulus *see* Jay
Gasterosteus *see* Stickleback
Gavia immer *see* Great Northern Diver
G. stellata *see* Red-throated Diver
Gillaroo (Salmo trutta) 134
Gull *see* Black-headed, Common, Great & Lesser Black-backed, Herring G.
Gentiana *see* Blue Gentian
Geomalcus *see* Kerry Slug
Germander Speedwell (Veronica chamaedrys), 18
Glasswort (Salicornia), 85
Glaucium *see* Yellow-horned Poppy
Globiocephala *see* Pilot Whale
Gobiesocidae *see* Suckerfish
Gobio *see* Gudgeon
Gobius *see* Goby
Goby, 86
Godwit *see* Bar-tailed, Black-tailed G.
Goldcrest (R. regulus), 35, 48, 91
Golden Eagle (Aquila chrysaetos), 142
Goldeneye (Bucephala clangula), 87
Golden Plover (Charadrius apricarius), 72, 95, 97, 101, 126, 141
Golden Samphire (Crithmum maritimum), 81
Goldfinch (C. carduelis), 34
Goose *see* Barnacle, Brent, Grey-lag, Whitefronted G.
Gorse (Ulex), 29, 47, 124, 164, 167
Grasshopper Warbler (Locustella naevia), 54, 161
Great Auk (Alca impennis), 82
Great Black-backed Gull (Larus marinus), 24, 82, 94, 102
Great Butterwort (Pinguicula grandiflora), 39, 106, 109
Great Crested Grebe (Podiceps cristatus), 70, 87, 115, 118, 142, 152, 155, 156
Great Northern Diver (Gavia immer), 87
Great Shearwater (Procellaria gravis), 90, 108
Great Tit (Parus major), 19, 35, 48
Grebe *see* Dabchick, Great Crested G.
Greenfinch (C. chloris), 18, 34
Grey Crow *see* Hooded Crow

Grey-lag Goose (A. anser), 72, 97
Grey Mullet *see* Mullet
Grey Seal (Halichoerus grypus), 89, 102, 109, 113, 125, 130, 138
Grey Squirrel (Sciurus carolinensis), 48, 147, 156, 157, 161
Grey Wagtail (Motacilla cinerea), 24, 60
Groundsel (Senecio vulgaris), 15, 18
Grouse (L. lagopus), 40
Gudgeon (G. gobio), 22
Guillemot (Uria aalge), 82, 94, 102, 103
Guelder Rose (Viburnum opulus), 121

Haematopus *see* Oystercatcher
Haddock (Melanogrammus aeglefinus), 89
Halichoerus *see* Grey Seal
Harbour Seal *see* Common Seal
Hare (Lepus timidus) *see also* Brown H., 18, 31, 40, 76
Hart's Tongue (Phyllitis scolopendrium), 15
Hawk *see* Kestrel, Sparrow Hawk
Hawkweed (Hieracium), 18, 26
Hawthorn (Crategus monogyna), 17, 27, 29, 35, 124, 164
Hazel (Corylus avellana), 43, 45, 47, 116, 117, 131, 147, 161
Heather (Erica cinerea), 37, 55, 56
Hedgehog (Erinaceus europaeus), 31, 40
Hedge Sparrow (Prunella modularis), 18, 19, 42
Helianthemum *see* Spotted Rockrose
Hemlock Spruce (Tsuga heterophylla), 106, 110, 131, 141, 144, 163
Heron (Ardea cinerea), *23*, 24, 71, 87
Herring Gull (Larus argentatus), 19, 24, 27, 82, 83, 91, 94, 95, 97, 101, 103, *143*
Hieracium *see* Hawkweed
Hippuris *see* Mare's Tail
Hirundo *see* Swallow
Holcus *see* Yorkshire Fog
Holly (Ilex aquifolium), 17, 39, 45, 47, 131, 147, 161, 163, 173
Homarus *see* Lobster
Hooded Crow (Corvus cornix), 34, 40, 91
Hordeum *see* Barley
Horse Chestnut (Aesculus hippocastaneum), 29, 47
Horse Mackerel *see* Scad
Horsetail (Equisetum), 51
House Martin (Delichon urbica), 35, 69
House Mouse (Mus musculus), 14, 18
Hydrobates *see* Storm Petrel
Hypnoid Saxifrage (Saxifraga hypnoides), 43, 117, 131

Ilex *see* Holly
Iris *see* Yellow Flag

Irish Deer (Cervus giganteus), 115
Irish Sandwort (Arenaria ciliata), 131
Irish Spurge (Euphorbia hyberna), 106, 109, 114
Irish Yew (Florencecourt Yew), 151, *153*

Jackdaw (Corvus monedula), 18, 27, 30, 34
Japanese Deer *see* Sika Deer
Jay (Garrulus glandarius), 50, 91
Juniperus communis, 169

Kerry Slug (Geomalcus maculosus), 109
Kestrel (Falco tinnunculus), 36, 42
Kidney Vetch (Anthyllis vulneraria), 103
Killarney Shad (Alosa fallax), 111
Kingfisher (Alcedo atthis), 24, 64, 97
Kittiwake (Rissa tridactyla), 82, 94, 102, 103
Knot (Calidris canuta), 95

Lacerta *see* Lizard
Lagopus *see* Grouse
Laminaria *see* Strap Wrack
Lamna *see* Porbeagle
Lamprey (Petromyzonidae), 62, 63
Lapwing (V. vanellus), 19, 29, 72, 88, 97
Larch (Larix), 45, 47, 110, 141, 144, 146, 160, 163, 167, 168, 169
Lark *see* Skylark
Larus argentatus *see* Herring Gull
L. canus *see* Common Gull
L. fuscus *see* Lesser Black-backed Gull
L. marinus *see* Great Black-backed Gull
L. ridibundus *see* Black-headed Gull
Lawson Cypress (Chamaecyparis lawsoniana), 144, 163, 167
Least Willow (Salix herbacea), 146
Leatherjacket *see* Cranefly
Leisler's Bat (Nyctalus leisleri), 30
Lemming (Dicrostonyx), 131
Lepus europaeus *see* Brown Hare
L. timidus *see* Hare
Lesser Black-backed Gull (Larus fuscus), 24, 83, 94, 102, 141
Leuciscus *see* Dace
Limonium *see* Sea Lavender
Limosa lapponica *see* Bar-tailed Godwit
L. Limosa *see* Black-tailed Godwit
Limpet (Patella), 78, *138*
Linnet (Carduelis cannabina), 34
Liparis *see* Sea Snail
Lithophyllum *see* Coralline
Little Tern (Sterna albifrons), 76, 77
Littorina *see* Winkle
Lizard (Lacerta vivipara), 13
Lobelia *see* Water Lobelia

Lobster (Homarus vulgaris), 80
Locustella *see* Grasshopper Warbler
Lolium *see* Ryegrass
London Pride *see* St. Patrick's Cabbage
Long-eared Bat (Plecotus auritus), 30
Long-eared Owl (Asio otus), 36
Long-tailed Duck (Clangula hyemalis), 87
Long-tailed Field Mouse *see* Woodmouse
Lotus *see* Bird's Foot Trefoil
Lousewort (Pedicularis sylvatica), 39
Lumbricus *see* Earthworm
Lutra *see* Otter
Lychnis *see* Ragged Robin
Lycoperdon *see* Puff-ball
Lysimachia *see* Yellow Loosestrife
Lythrum *see* Purple Loosestrife

Mackerel (S. scomber), 89
Mackey's Heath (Erica mackaiana), 120
Magpie (P. pica), 18, 19, 34
Maidenhair Fern (Adiantum capillis-veneris), 43, 117
Mallard (Anas platyrhynchos), *21*, 66, 70, 72, 87, 91, 95, 97, 111, 118, 122, 127, 140, 149, 156, 166, 169, 173
Malus *see* Crab Apple
Mare's Tail (Hippuris vulgaris), 21, 68
Maritime Pine (Pinus pinaster), 131
Marsh Marigold (Caltha palustris), 52
Martes *see* Pine Marten
Martin *see* House M., Sand M.
Marram (Ammophila maritima), 75
Mayfly (Ephemeroptera), 22, 52, 59, 61
Meadow Pipit (Anthus pratensis), 27, 29, 41, 76, 94, 126
Meadowsweet (Filipendula ulmaria), 52
Mediterranean Heath (Erica mediterranea), 121, *128*
Melanitta *see* Scoter
Melanogrammus *see* Haddock
Meles *see* Badger
Mentha *see* Watermint
Merganser (Mergus serrator), 70, 71, 87, 111, 118, 124
Merlin (Falco columbarius), 36
Minnow (P. phoxinus), 10, 22, 62
Mistle Thrush (Turdus viscivorus), 18, 19, 35, 42
Mole (Talpa), 10
Molinia *see* Moorland Grass
Monkeypuzzle (Araucaria), 92, 171
Monterey Pine (Pinus radiata), 99, 110, 136
Moorhen (Gallinula chloropus), 21, 24, 54, 66, 70, 91, 97, 118, 152, 173
Moorland Gass (Molinia caerulea), 56
Morone *see* Bass
Motacilla alba *see* Pied Wagtail
M. cinerea *see* Grey Wagtail

Mountain Ash (Sorbus aucuparia), 39, 42, 47
Mountain Hare *see* Hare
Mouse *see* House M., Wood M.
Mugil *see* Mullet
Mullet (Mugil labrosus), 24, 86, 100, 105
Muscicapa hypoleuca *see* Pied Flycatcher
M. striata *see* Spotted Flycatcher
Mus *see* House Mouse
Mussel (Mytilus edulis), 24, 112, 146, 149
Mustela *see* Stoat
Mute Swan (Cygnus olor), 21, 70, 97, 101
Mysis relicta, 117
Myosotis *see* Forget-me-not
Mytilus *see* Mussel

Narthecium *see* Bog Asphodel
Nasturtium *see* Watercress
Natterjack (Bufo calamitas), 13, 112
Neotinea *see* Close-flowered Orchid
Nettle (Urtica), 18
Newt (Triturus vulgaris), 13, 53
Nightjar (Caprimulgus europaeus), 41
Norway Spruce (Picea abies), 134, 141, 155, 156, 161, 165, 169
Numenius *see* Curlew
Nuphar *see* Yellow Water Lily
Nyctalus *see* Leisler's Bat
Nyctea *see* Snowy Owl
Nymphaea *see* White Water Lily

Oak (Quercus), 29, 45, 47, 92, 96, 106, 109, 110, 116, 121, 126, 131, 141, 144, 155, 156, 160, 161, 163, 165, 167, 169, 173
Odonata *see* Dragonfly
Oenanthe *see* Dropwort
O. oenanthe *see* Wheatear
Ononis *see* Rest-harrow
Ophiuroidea *see* Brittle Starfish
Oryctolagus *see* Rabbit
Osier (Salix viminalis), 52
Osmerus *see* Smelt
Osmunda *see* Royal Fern
Ostrea *see* Oyster
Odontogadus *see* Whiting
Otanthus *see* Cotton Weed
Otter (L. lutra), 64, 91
Owl *see* Barn O., Long-eared O.
Oyster (Ostrea edulis), 112
Oystercatcher (Haematopus ostralegus), 19, 76, 88, 95

Palinurus *see* Crawfish
Papaver *see* Poppy
Parus ater *see* Coal Tit
P. caeruleus *see* Blue Tit
P. major *see* Great Tit
Partridge (P. perdix), 35
Passer *see* Sparrow
Patella *see* Limpet
Pearl-bordered Fritillary (Argynnis euphrosyne), 117
Perca *see* Perch
Perch (Perca fluviatilis), 10, 22, 62, 66, 97, 110, 149, 156, 157, 162
Perdix *see* Partridge

Petromyzon *see* Lamprey, Sea Lamprey
Phalacrocorax aristotelis *see* Shag
P. carbo *see* Cormorant
Phalaropus *see* Red-necked Phalarope
Phasianus *see* Pheasant
Pheasant (Phasianus colchicus), 35, 50, 54
Phleum *see* Catstail
Phocaena *see* Porpoise
Phoca *see* Common Seal
Phoenicurus *see* Redstart
Phoxinus *see* Minnow
Phragmites *see* Reed
Phyllitis *see* Hart's Tongue
Phylloscopus collybita *see* Chiffchaff
P. trochilus *see* Willow Warbler
Pica *see* Magpie
Picea abies *see* Norway Spruce
P. sitchensis *see* Sitka Spruce
Pied Flycatcher (Muscicapa hypoleucos), 102
Pied Wagtail (Motacilla alba), 15, 24, 27, 76, 91
Pig (Sus scrofa), 13
Pigeon *see also* Rock Dove, Wood P., 15
Pike (Esox lucius), 10, 22, 62, 64, 66, 97, 110, 149, 156, 157, 162
Pilot Whale (Globiocephala melaena), 89
Pine *see* Corsican, Contorta, Maritime, Monterey, Scots
Pine marten (M. martes), 48, 116, 117, 144
Pinguicula grandiflora *see* Great Butterwort
P. vulgaris *see* Common Butterwort
Pintail (Anas acuta), 87, *88,* 95
Pinus contorta *see* Contorta Pine
P. nigra *see* Corsican Pine
P. pinaster *see* Maritime Pine
P. radiata *see* Monterey Pine
P. sylvestris *see* Scots Pine
Pipefish (Syngnathidae), 86, 108
Pipewort (Eriocaulon septangulare), *123,* 125, 129
Pipistrelle (P. pipistrellus), 30
Pipit *see* Meadow P., Rock P.
Plaice (Pleuronectes platessa), 86
Plane Tree (Platanus acerifolia), 91
Plantago *see* Sea Plantain
Platanus *see* Plane Tree
Plecoptera *see* Stonefly
Plecotus *see* Long-eared Bat
Plectrophenax *see* Snow Bunting
Pleuronectes flesus *see* Flounder
P. platessa *see* Plaice
Plover *see* Golden P., Ringed P.
Pochard (Aythya ferina), 72, 97, 139, 166
Podiceps cristatus *see* Great Crested Grebe
P. ruficollis *see* Dabchick
Pollack (Gadus pollachius), 80
Pollan (Coregonus), 69, 117, 141, 152
Polyporus, *46*

Pondweed (Potamogeton), 66, 68
Poplar (Populus), 106, 141, 163
Poppy (Papaver), 26, 27
Porbeagle (Lamna nasus), 89
Porpoise (P. phocoena), 89
Potamogeton *see* Pondweed
Potato, 27
Potentilla *see* Tormentil
Prunella *see* Hedge Sparrow
Prunus *see* Blackthorn
Procellaria diomedea *see* Cory's Shearwater
P. gravis *see* Great Shearwater
P. grisea *see* Sooty Shearwater
Pseudotsuga *see* Douglas Fir
Puff-ball (Lycoperdon), *170*
Puffin (Fratercula arctica), 83, 102, 113, 129
Puffinus *see* Shearwater
Pteridium *see* Bracken
Purple Loosestrife (Lythrum salicaria), 132
Pygmy Shrew (Sorex minutus), 31, 40
Pyrrhocorax *see* Chough
Pyrrhula *see* Bullfinch

Quaking Grass (Briza media), 27
Quercus *see* Oak
Quicken Tree *see* Mountain Ash
Q. suber *see* Cork Oak

Rabbit (Oryctolagus cuniculus), 18, 31, 40, 76, 91
Ragged Robin (Lychnis flos-cuculi), 52
Ragwort (Senecio jacobaea), 27, 28, *33*
Rainbow Trout (Salmo irideus), 149, 164
Rallus *see* Water Rail
Rana *see* Frog
Rangifer *see* Reindeer
Ranunculus *see* Buttercup
Rat (Rattus norvegicus), 14, 18, 20, 64
Raven (Corvus corax), 40, 82, 97
Razorbill (Alca torda), 82, 94, 102, 103
Red-breasted Merganser *see* Merganser
Red Cedar (Thuja plicata), 136, 156, 163, 171
Red Deer (Cervus elephas), 13, 30, 40, 96, 109, 135, 144, 150
Red-necked Phalarope (Phalaropus lobatus), 130
Redshank (Tringa totanus), 71, 95, 141
Red Squirrel (Sciurus vulgaris), 48, 91, 102, 158
Redstart (P. phoenicurus), 102
Red-throated Diver (Gavia stellata), 67, 87, 115, 136
Redwing (Turdus musicus), 35
Redwood (Sequoia sempervirens), 144, 171
Reed (Phragmites communis), 51, 52, 54, 55, 65, 68
Reed Bunting (Emberiza schoeniculus), 54
Reindeer (Rangifer tardanus), 131
Regulus *see* Goldcrest
Rest Harrow (Ononis repens), 75
Rhododendron ponticum, 110, 126, 129

Ricegrass (Spartina townsendii), 85
Ring Ouzel (Turdus torquata), 42
Ringed Plover (Charadrius hiaticula), 71, 76
Rissa *see* Kittiwake
River Limpet (Ancylastrum fluviatile), 59, 61
Roach (R. rutilus), 62, 150, 152
Robin (Erithacus rubecula), 18, 35
Rock Dove (Columba livia), 82
Rock Pipit (Anthus spinoletta), 76
Rook (Corvus frugilegus), 18, 19, 25, 27, 30
Rosa *see* Wild Rose
Roseate Tern (Sterna dougalii), 77
Roseroot (Sedum rosea), 146
Rowan *see* Mountain Ash
Royal Fern (Osmunda regalis), 39, 132, 136
Rubus *see* Bramble
Rudd (Scardinius erythrophthalmus), 10, 62, 110, 157
Rush (Juncus), 52
Rusty-back (Ceterarch officinarum), 15
Rutilus *see* Roach
Rye Grass (Lolium), 27

St. Dabeoc's Heath (Daboecia cantabrica), 120
St. Patrick's Cabbage (Saxifraga spathularis), *104,* 106, 109, 114, 136
Salicornia *see* Glasswort
Salix *see* Willow
S. herbacea *see* Least Willow
S. repens *see* Creeping Willow
S. viminalis *see* Osier
Salmo irideus *see* Rainbow Trout
S. salar *see* Salmon
S. trutta *see* Trout, Sea Trout
Salmon (Salmo salar), 12, 62, 91, 96, 99, 105, 107, 110, 113, 118, 119, 120, 122, 126, 128, 132, 136, 137, 139, 140, 146, 147, 151, 169, 171, 172
Salvelinus *see* Char
Sandhopper (Amphipoda), 75
Sand Martin (R. riparia), 69
Sand Pansy (Viola curtisii), 75
Sandpiper *see* Common Sandpiper
Sandwich Tern (Sterna sandvicensis), 77, 127
Saxicola *see* Whinchat
Saxifraga nivalis *see* Clustered Alpine Saxifrage
S. spathularis *see* St. Patrick's Cabbage
Scad (T. trachurus), 86
Scald Crow *see* Hooded Crow
Scardinius *see* Rudd
Scaup (Aythya marila), 87
Scilla *see* Bluebell
Scirpus lacustris *see* Bullrush
S. triqueter *see* Triangular Club-rush
Sciurus carolinensis *see* Grey Squirrel
S. vulgaris *see* Red Squirrel
Scolopax *see* Woodcock
Scomber *see* Mackerel
Scoter (Melanitta nigra), 87, 112, 152

Scots Pine (Pinus sylvestris), 47, 110, 124, 131, 136, 155, 161, 165, 167, 169
Sea Anemone (Anthozoa), 80
Sea Aster (Aster tripolium), 85
Sea Beet (Beta maritima), 81
Sea Campion (Silene maritima), 75, 81, 103
Sea Holly (Eryngium maritimum), 75
Seal *see* Common S., Grey S.
Sea Lamprey (Petromyzon marinus), 120
Sea Lavender (Limonium), 85
Sea Pink (Armeria maritima), 81, 103, *111*, 113, 119
Sea Plantain (Plantago maritima), 119, 125
Sea Squirt (Tunicata), 76
Sea Snail (Liparis), 86
Sea Trout (Salmo trutta), 22, 86, 92
Sea Urchin (Echinoidea), 109
Sedge (Cyperaceae), 52
Sedge Warbler (Acrocephalus schoenobaenus), 54
Sedum *see* Stonecrop
S. roseum *see* Roseroot
Senecio jacobaea *see* Ragwort
S. vulgaris *see* Groundsel
Sequoia *see* Redwood
Sequoiadendron *see* Wellingtonia
Shad (Alosa), 86
Shag (Phalacrocorax aristotelis), 77, 82, 83, 87, 102, 103
Shearwater (P. puffinus), 83, 102, 113, 144
Shelduck (T. tadorna), 87, 94, 95
Shepherd's Purse (Capsella bursa-pastoris), 18
Shore Crab (Carcinus maenas), 24, 100
Shoveler (Spatula clypeata), 87, 95, 139, 169
Shrew *see* Pygmy Shrew
Shrimp (Natantia), 79
Sika Deer (Cervus nippon), 40, 96, 109, 150
Silene *see* Sea Campion
Silver Fir (Abies alba), 106, 110, 116, 121, 131, 156, 165, 171
Simulid *see* Blackfly
Sitka Spruce (Picea sitchensis), 48, *49*, 92, 106, 110, 121, 134, 136, 155, 156, 163, 167, 168
Skua (Stercorariidae), 90, 113
Skylark (Alauda arvensis), 41, 76, 94
Sloe *see* Blackthorn
Small Tortoiseshell (Aglais urticae), *116*
Smelt (Osmerus eperlanus), 114, 118
Snipe (Capella gallinago), 40, 41, 97, 122
Snow Bunting (Plectrophenax nivalis), 76
Snowy Owl (Nyctea scandiaca), 130
Sole (S. solea), 86
Somateria *see* Eider
Sonchus *see* Sow Thistle
Song Thrush (Turdus ericetorum), 18, 35, 42
Sooty Shearwater (Procellaria grisea), 108
Sorbus *see* Mountain Ash

Sorex *see* Pygmy Shrew
Sow Thistle (Sonchus), 18, 26
Spanish Chestnut (Castanea sativa), 92, 146
Sparrow (Passer domesticus), 15, 25
Sparrow Hawk (Accipiter nisus), 36
Spartina *see* Ricegrass
Sphagnum, 55, 56
Spilosoma *see* Ermine
Spindle Tree (Euonymus europaeus), 121
Spiranthes *see* Threefold Lady's Tresses
Spirorbis, 76
Spleenwort (Asplenium trichomanes), 15
Spotted Flycatcher (Muscicapa striata), 36
Spotted Rockrose (Helianthemum guttatum), 125
Squirrel *see* Grey S., Red S.
Starfish (Asterias), 108
Starling (Sturnus vulgaris), 15, 25, 27, 30, 34, 91, 95
Stercorariidae *see* Skua
Sterna albifrons *see* Little Tern
S. dougalii *see* Roseate Tern
S. hirundo *see* Common Tern
S. macrura *see* Arctic Tern
S. sandvicensis *see* Sandwich Tern
Stickleback (Gasterosteus), 22, 62, 66, 100
Stoat (Mustela erminea), 32, 40, 48
Stonecrop (Sedum), *41*
Stonefly (Plecoptera), 59, 61
Storm Petrel (Hydrobates pelagicus), 83, 108, 112, 113, 128
Strap Wrack (Laminaria), 78
Sturnus *see* Starling
Suckerfish (Gobiesocidae), 108
Sugar Beet, 27
Sula *see* Gannet
Round-leaved Sundew
(Drosera rotundifolia), 39
Sus *see* Pig
Swallow (Hirundo rustica), 35, 69
Swan *see* Bewick's S., Mute S., Whooper S.
Swift (A. apus), 15, 35, 42, 69
Sycamore (Acer pseudoplatanus), 27, 29, 47, 116, 155, 160, 161
Sylvia communis *see* Whitethroat
Syngnathidae *see* Pipefish

Tadorna *see* Shelduck
Talpa *see* Mole
Taraxacum *see* Dandelion
Taxus *see* Yew
Teal (Anas crecca), 70, 72, 87, 95, 97, 111, 118, 122, 140
Tench (T. tinca), 62, 159
Tern *see* Arctic T., Common T., Little T., Roseate T., Sandwich T.
Thistle (Cirsium), 26, 27, 28
Threefold Lady's Tresses (Spiranthes romanzoffiana), 140
Thrush *see* Mistle T., Song T.
Thuja *see* Red Cedar
Tinca *see* Tench
Tipula *see* Cranefly

Tit *see* Blue T., Coal T., Great T.
Toad *see* Natterjack
Top Shell (Calliostoma), *81*
Tormentil (Potentilla erecta), 39
Trachurus *see* Scad
Transparent Burnet (Zygaena purpuralis), 117
Tree Creeper (Certhia familiaris), 35, 50
Triangular Club-rush (Scirpus triqueter), 115
Trichophorum *see* Deergrass
Trichoptera *see* Caddis
Tringa hypoleucos *see* Common Sandpiper
T. totanus *see* Redshank
Triturus *see* Newt
Troglodytes *see* Wren
Tsuga *see* Hemlock Spruce
Tufted Duck (Aythya fuligula), 69, 70, 72, 118, 124, 139, 140, 156, 166
Turdus ericetorum *see* Song Thrush
T. merula *see* Blackbird
T. musicus *see* Redwing
T. pilaris *see* Fieldfare
T. torquatus *see* Ring Ouzel
T. viscivorus *see* Mistle Thrush
Twaite Shad (Alosa fallax), 171
Tyto *see* Barn Owl

Ulex *see* Gorse
Ulmus *see* Elm
Uria *see* Guillemot
Ursus *see* Bear
Urtica *see* Nettle

Vulpes *see* Fox
Vole *see* Bank Vole, Water Rat
Vicia *see* Vetch
Veronica becca-bunga *see* Brooklime
V. chamaedrys *see* Germander Speedwell
Vanellus *see* Lapwing
Vetch (Vicia), 26
Viburnum *see* Guelder Rose
Viola curtisii *see* Sand Pansy
Violet (Viola), *38*

Wagtail *see* Grey W., Pied W.
Wall Rue (Asplenium ruta muraria), 15
Warbler *see* Grasshopper W., Sedge W., Willow W.
Water-boatman (Corixidae), 52, 61, 65
Water Buttercup (Ranunculus), 21
Watercress (Nasturtium officinale), 21, 61
Waterhen *see* Moorhen
Water Lily *see* White W., Yellow W.
Water Lobelia (Lobelia dortmanna), 68
Water Louse (Asellus), 22, 61
Water Mint (Mentha aquatica), 52
Water Rail (Rallus aquaticus), 54
Water Rat (Arvicola amphibius), 64
Water Snail, 22
Weasel *see* Stoat
Wellingtonia (Sequoiadendron gigantea), 50
Whale *see* Pilot Whale
Wheatear (O. oenanthe), 41, 76

Whelk (Buccinum undatum), 146
Whinchat (Saxicola rubetra), 161
Whitefish *see* Pollan
White-fronted Goose (Anser albifrons), 72, 94, 98, 101, 115, 122, 132, 164
Whiting (Odontogadus merlangus), 89
Whitethroat (Sylvia communis), 35
White Trout *see* Sea Trout
White Water-lily (Nymphaea alba), 56, 66
Whooper Swan (C. cygnus), 72, 93, 97, 122, 132
Wigeon (Anas penelope), 72, 87, 94, 97, 112, 140, 145
Wildcat (Felis silvestris), 10
Wild Garlic (Allium ursinum), 45
Wild Rose (Rosa canina), 27
Willow (Salix), 39, 47, 171
Willow Herb (Epilobium), 18
Willow Warbler (Phylloscopus trochilus), 19, 35
Winkle (Littorina), 79
Wolf (Canis lupus), 13, 30
Wood Anemone (Anemone nemorosa), 45
Woodcock (Scolopax rusticola), 40, 50
Woodmouse (Apodemus sylvatica), 14, 18, 31
Wood Pigeon (Columba palumbus), 18, 19, 34, 50
Wrasse (Labridae), 80, 86
Wren (T. troglodytes), 19

Yellow Flag (Iris pseud-acorus), 52, 147
Yellow Hammer (Emberiza citrinella), 34
Yellow-horned Poppy (Glaucium flavum), 75
Yellow Loosestrife (Lysimachia vulgaris), 159
Yellow Water-lily (Nuphar lutea), 21
Yew (Taxus baccata), 29, 47, 169
Yorkshire Fog (Holcus lanatus), 27

Zostera *see* Eelgrass
Zygaena *see* Transparent Burnet